❦❦❦ PASSING ON

This excellent hotel is very ancient. Even in King Clovis' time people died in it in a number of beds. Now they are dying there in 559 beds. Factory like, of course. Where production is so enormous an individual death is not so nicely carried out; but then that doesn't matter. It is quantity that counts. Who cares anything today for a finely finished death? No one. Even the rich, who could after all afford this luxury of dying in full detail, are beginning to be careless and indifferent; the wish to have a death of one's own is growing ever rarer. A while yet, and it will be just as rare as a life of one's own. Heavens, it's all there. One arrives, one finds a life, ready made, one has only to put it on. One wants to leave or one is compelled to; anyway, no effort: *Voila, votre mort, monsieur.* One dies just as it comes; one dies the death that belongs to the disease one has (for since one has come to know all diseases, one knows too, that the different lethal terminations belong to the diseases and not to the people; and the sick person has so to speak nothing to do).

RILKE, *The Notebooks of Malte Laurids Brigge*

PASSING ON

The Social Organization of Dying

DAVID SUDNOW

PRENTICE-HALL, INC.
Englewood Cliffs, New Jersey

Library of Congress Catalog Card Number: 67–12201

Printed in the United States of America   C–65271

Current printing (last digit):

17   16   15

PRENTICE-HALL INTERNATIONAL, INC., London
PRENTICE-HALL OF AUSTRALIA, PTY. LTD., Sydney
PRENTICE-HALL OF CANADA, LTD., Toronto
PRENTICE-HALL OF INDIA (PRIVATE) LTD., New Delhi
PRENTICE-HALL OF JAPAN, INC., Tokyo

PREFACE

❧❧❧ THIS STUDY IS, first and foremost, an ethnography. It seeks to depict the heretofore undescribed social organization of "death work" and to do so from the perspective of those persons in our society intimately involved, as a matter of daily occupational life, in caring for the "dying" and the "dead"—members of a hospital staff. Research of this kind would not have been possible were it not for the exceedingly gracious cooperation given me by numerous persons at all staff levels at "County" and "Cohen" Hospitals. In accord with my promises to them, I cannot thank individuals by name nor identify the institutions directly. Whatever the reasons for the relatively limited amount of ethnography that goes on in medical hospital settings, accessibility seems not to be at fault. I found members of the medical professions, as well as other hospital employees, more than willing to have their activities scrutinized by an outsider. To those who so patiently put up with my snooping about and my naive questioning, I am grateful.

Erving Goffman, as director of the study when it was prepared as a doctoral dissertation at the University of California, Berkeley, provided the initial intellectual stimulus for my venture into field work generally, and offered many suggestions on ways to improve the manuscript. I have tried in footnotes to indicate my indebtedness to him, at least with respect to particular ethnographic and theoretical issues.

I have benefited at various points in the conduct of the research from my discussions with Sheldon Messinger, Harvey Sacks, Roy Turner, and Helen Pat Gouldner. An earlier version of Chapter 4 was presented at a conference held by Harold Garfinkel of UCLA in the summer of 1965. My indebtedness to Professor Garfinkel will, I hope, be clear to those who know his work. I do not claim, however, that this study is well representative of "ethnomethodological" sociology, though should that be at all true, I would be very pleased.

The Medical Care Research Center of the Social Science Institute, Washington University, St. Louis, gained access for me at "Cohen" Hospital, provided partial support for portions of my research, and generously made office space available to me. I am particularly grateful to Rod Coe and Al Wessen of MCRC.

The most continuous financial support during the period of the investigation was provided when I was a graduate student by a National Institute of Mental Health Fellowship (NIMH–8268). I am grateful to John Clausen, who served as director of the fellowship program. Anselm Strauss of the University of California School of Nursing provided funds during the summer of 1963, when this study was begun. I am grateful for the opportunity he created.

DAVID SUDNOW

CONTENTS

❦❦❦ PASSING ON

ONE

Introduction

❧ ❧ ❧ DEATH IS a major topic of concern among anthropologists, physicians, psychiatrists, artists, and men of literature, but scarcely any attention has been given to the empirical investigation of settings of death and dying in contemporary Western society.[1] The anthropological literature is replete with discussions of death rituals in the non-Western world, in fact many of the most central issues of anthropological theory: kinship, the role of ceremony, religious organization, principles of inheritance, sacred-secular distinctions, have been formulated in the course of the examination of ethnographic materials dealing with death.[2] With the exception of several recent popular expositions of American funeral

[1] The best general source for literary treatments of death is F. Hoffman, "Mortality and Modern Literature," in H. Feifel, ed., *The Meaning of Death* (New York: McGraw-Hill Book Company, 1959), pp. 133–157. For a recent contextual analysis of morbidity themes in literature, see Leslie Fiedler, *Love and Death in the American Novel* (New York: Meridian Books, 1960). As is often the case, literary descriptions far exceed, in detail and sophistication, those of professional academics. Nowhere in the academic literature are death scenes described as vividly as in Hemingway's *A Natural History of the Dead,* or Mailer's *The Naked and the Dead.* And there is Orwell's "How the Poor Die," Rilke's *The Notebooks of Malte Laurids Brigge,* Tennyson's poem "The Children's Hospital," Tolstoy's *War and Peace,* and his "The Death of Ivan Ilyich," James Agee's *Death in the Family,* and Cather's *Death Comes for the Archbishop,* to mention but a few.

[2] The anthropological literature on death and rituals surrounding its occurrence is too extensive to readily cite. The works of Durkheim, Frazer, Tylor, Evans-Pritchard, Malinowski, Radcliffe-Brown, Van Gennep, Hertz, and Gluckman are obviously central. A relatively complete collection of death practices in non-Western societies may be found in E. Bendmann, *Death Customs* (New York: Alfred A. Knopf, Inc., 1930). The most serious study of death ritual by an anthropologist within the past twenty-five years is Jack Goody's *Death, Property and the Ancestors* (Stanford: Stanford University Press, 1962).

1

practices, and the classic discussion of death symbolism by W. L. Warner, death in modern society has been largely neglected as a matter of sociological investigation.[3] Psychiatric interest has traditionally been guided by Freudian concerns with "death instincts," "fear of death," "aggression," and the psychodynamic significance of grief.[4]

The growing literature on the social organization of the hospital —that major setting of dying in our society—contains virtually no descriptions of the place of dying and death in such work organizations. Sociological analyses of the medical profession treat of death only casually, with little attention given to the physician's ways of arranging his care of the "terminally ill" patient.[5] Recent collections of articles on death are

[3] Particularly Leroy Bowman, *The American Funeral* (New York: Paperback Library, Inc., 1964), J. Mitford, *The American Way of Death* (New York: Simon and Schuster, Inc., 1963), and R. Harner, *The High Cost of Dying* (New York: Crowell-Collier & Macmillan, Inc., 1963). Warner's analysis is found in *The Living and the Dead* (New Haven: Yale University Press, 1959). There have been sociological studies of occupational features of undertaker work, notable among which is R. Habenstein, *The American Funeral Director: A Study in the Sociology of Work,* unpublished doctoral dissertation, University of Chicago, 1954. A recent exception to the general absence of empirical research on death by sociologists is the work of Glaser and Strauss. See especially R. Glaser and A. Strauss, "Temporal Aspects of Dying as a Nonscheduled Status Passage," *American Journal of Sociology,* 81 (July, 1965), 48–59, and their recent book, *Awareness of Dying* (Chicago: Aldine Publishing Co., 1965).

There is a considerable literature on death and the family, but very little of it is based on concrete empirical investigations of family interaction in times of death, and most discussion is largely couched in psychiatric terms. Especially see T. Eliot, "The Bereaved Family," *Annals of the American Academy of Political and Social Science,* 160 (March, 1932), 184–190, K. Davis, "The Widow and the Social Structure," *American Sociological Review,* 5 (August, 1940), 635–647, H. Becker, "The Sorrow of Bereavement," *Journal of Abnormal and Social Psychology,* 27 (1933), 391–410, and G. Gorer, *Death, Grief and Mourning* (Garden City: Doubleday & Company, Inc., 1965).

[4] This literature, as that of the anthropologists, is quite extensive. The most prominent sources are S. Freud, "Thoughts for the Times on War and Death," *Collected Papers* (London: Hogarth Press, 1948), Vol. 4; *Civilization and Its Discontents* (London: Hogarth Press, 1933); *Totem and Taboo* (New York: W. W. Norton & Company, Inc., 1952); *Mourning and Melancholia* (London: Hogarth Press, 1957); S. Anthony, *The Child's Discovery of Death* (London: Routledge & Kegan Paul, Ltd., 1940), W. Bromberg and P. Schilder, "The Attitude of Psychoneurotics towards Death," *Psychoanalytic Review,* 23, No. 1 (International Universities Press, 1955); M. Klein, "Mourning and Its Relation to Manic-Depressive States," *International Journal of Psychoanalysis,* 21 (1940), 125–153; E. Lindemann, "Symptomatology and Management of Acute Grief," *American Journal of Psychiatry* (September, 1944), 101–141.

[5] The recently published collection of articles on hospital social structure, edited by E. Friedson, *The Hospital in Modern Society* (New York: Free Press of Glencoe, Inc., 1963), contains no discussions of death, nor is there significant treatment of the topic in any other research on this institution, with the slight exception of the attention given "dying" by R. Fox, *Experiment Perilous* (New York: Free Press of Glencoe, Inc., 1959). The most modern vivid account of the general hospital available, with exceedingly close attention given to details of daily hospital life, is Jan de Hartog's semifictional *The Hospital* (New York: Atheneum Publishers, 1964).

Research on medical students contains only minimal reference to the relevance of "dying" and "death" in environments of learning. See H. Becker *et al., Boys in*

given almost exclusively to semiphilosophical discussions and attitudinal research.[6] Only in the medical literature, those occasional articles written by practicing physicians about the social organization of their own circumstances of practice and the practically motivated researches of nursing personnel, does death regularly appear as a matter of interest.[7]

Nowhere do we have an ethnography of death, descriptions of how dead bodies are handled in hospitals, how care is given "dying" patients, how members of deceased patients' families are informed of the deaths of their relatives, how the social organization of the hospital is affected by and affects the occurrence of deaths within its confines. This study seeks to provide such an ethnography, based on field observations in two hospital settings, a large, urban West Coast charity institution, and a Midwestern, private, general hospital. The former setting will be referred to throughout the report as "County," the latter as "Cohen."

In both settings, in the role of a "nonparticipant observer," I have sought to get close to occasions of "dying" and "death," record what transpires in the behavior of staff members of the institutions on such occasions, and analyze some of the general features of that behavior. My central effort has been to locate "death" and "dying" as organizationally relevant events, conceive of their handling as governed by the practically organized work considerations of hospital personnel and ward social organization, and sketch out certain themes which appear to bring together a set of observed facts about social practices relating to "dying" and "death."

The most extensive field observation was conducted at County, and most of the following report concerns the social organization of this institution and the place of "dying" and "death" within it. After nine months in the field, the possibility arose to do observations elsewhere. Having obtained what I felt to be a fairly complete view of the social structure at County, I decided to investigate a quite different kind of setting—one

White (Chicago: University of Chicago Press, 1961), and R. K. Merton, G. Reader, and P. Kendall, eds., _The Student Physician_ (Cambridge: Harvard University Press, 1957). Talcott Parsons' famous articles on illness and the medical profession contain only indirect references to death and dying; his recent paper, "Death in American Society" has, as its central thesis, the notion that death is avoided, both by members of the society and investigators, for it constitutes a central threat to the stability of the social system in a society based on the Protestant Ethic of achievement.

[6] H. Feifel, _op. cit._, and R. Fulton, ed., _Death and Identity_ (New York: John Wiley & Sons, Inc., 1965). For serious collections of major philosophical positions on death, see J. Choron, _Death and Western Thought_ (New York: Collier Books, 1963), and A. Flew, _Body, Mind and Death_ (New York: The Macmillan Company, 1964).

[7] Especially, R. Bulger, "The Dying Patient and His Doctor," _Harvard Medical Alumni Bulletin_, 34, No. 23 (1960); V. E. Frenkl, _The Doctor and Soul_ (New York: Alfred A. Knopf, Inc., 1955); O. Guttentag, "The Meaning of Death in Medical Theory," _Stanford Medical Bulletin_, 17, No. 4 (1959); A. H. Solnit, "Psychologic Considerations in the Management of Deaths on Pediatric Hospital Services," _Pediatrics_, 24, No. 1, 106–115; C. K. Aldrich, "The Dying Patient's Grief," _Journal of the American Medical Association_, 184, No. 5 (1963).

where, in comparison to County, private physicians played a prominent role in daily hospital life; where, unlike County, with its chiefly lower-class patients, the largest proportion of patients were middle- and upper middle-class (on occasion, members of traditional "old families" used Cohen Hospital). Approximately five months of field work was done at Cohen. The following tables, taken from hospital annual reports for the years 1962 and 1963, summarize some demographic information about the two settings:

TABLE I

Average Daily Census

COUNTY	COHEN
369	438

TABLE II

Annual Number of Discharges and Deaths Per Year

	COUNTY	COHEN
Discharges	17,900	14,908
Deaths	985	419
Per cent	5.5	2.8

TABLE III

Average Length of Stay in Acute Divisions, in Days

COUNTY	COHEN
6.2	9.1

TABLE IV

Religious Composition of Patient Population, in Per Cent

	COUNTY	COHEN
Catholic	39	23
Protestant	70.4	45
Jewish	.5	31
Other	.1	1.0

TABLE V

Racial Composition of Patient Population, in Per Cent

	COUNTY	COHEN
White	59	88
Negro	40	12
Other	1	—

The two institutions were of similar overall size. The social-class composition of their patient populations, however, was noticeably different. County was very much a lower-class establishment, and Cohen very decidedly a middle-class institution. The slightly higher death rate at County (and a 2.7 per cent differential would be considered by physicians as substantial with respect to such matters) is at least partially an artifact of the circumstance that at County there is a very active Emergency Unit, where accident victims are brought by the police department, while the Emergency Room at Cohen is used only infrequently. A sizeable proportion of the total number of deaths at County, over 30 per cent, occur as the result of accidents, suicides, and cases where no period of hospitalization preceded the death. The class "dead on arrival" ("DOA") which I shall discuss in detail in Chapter 4, accounts for most of these deaths. Discounting their influence on the total death percentage, the two institutions had roughly the same death rates, with only a slightly greater proportion of deaths-per-bed at County.

Throughout the report, central attention is given to "dying" and "death" at County. My concern in making observations at Cohen was essentially to provide a comparative basis so as to be able to place partially in perspective the generality of the observations I had made at County. My references to practices at Cohen are intended to provide the reader with a sense of the variability that obtains in death practices in different hospitals. The study is first of all an investigation of death in the county hospital setting, and while County is not claimed to be representative of all such charity organizations, it most definitely appears to be in a class distinct from the private hospital. At every point in my investigations I found disparate practices between the two institutions, not only with respect to the treatment of "dying" patients, but with regard to a wide range of aspects of medical care. Physicians were, like sociologists, sensitive to both regional and social-class variations in modes of medical practice, careful to qualify their discussions of a given procedure or philosophy with such terms as "at least in the midwest," "in this part of the country," "in these kinds of hospitals." They were acutely attuned to variations said to derive from differing training careers, variations not only in general matters of medical philosophy, but with respect to detailed technical procedures. In different parts of the country different anesthetics are said to be used, different surgical techniques employed, different procedures followed in diagnostic conferences and decision-making. In conducting observations at the two institutions and placing those made at one against the context of those made in the other, I hope partially to have taken cognizance of this variability.

The observations upon which the report is based were obtained over a period of one and a half years, during which time I spent nearly the entire work week in the hospital. Time was spent on all three work shifts at County, with the most extensive participation during the day and evening shifts. Access to the hospitals was gained through formal administrative channels, in both instances through the Director of Nursing and the Chiefs of Medicine and Surgery. Personnel at this level were informed that the concern of the research was to investigate how staff members handled the treatment of "dying" patients. On the wards themselves, my own accounts of my interests ranged from rather detailed discussions, particularly with members of the medical staff, to only casual accounts like "I'm just interested in what you do here." In all, approximately 200–250 deaths were directly witnessed.

My procedure involved, initially, the location of those wards in the hospital which, according to daily census reports, had the highest number of deaths. In Chapter 3 I discuss some features of these wards. I was introduced, by upper-echelon administrators, to the personnel in charge of these areas, as a "sociologist studying the social organization of the hospital." Gradually, over the course of several weeks I became acquainted with all members of the staff, from orderlies to resident physicians. At County, I was not required to dress as a physician, but wore a business suit, with the exception of those times when I was in the Emergency Unit and during my observations in surgery and the delivery rooms. At Cohen, I was asked to wear a resident's gown, which I found had the advantage of making me less subject to queries from staff members and the disadvantage of leaving me open to a variety of requests by patients and their families.

The bulk of my time was spent watching and listening. When possible to do so unobstrusively, I took notes in a small book. In other situations I made a practice of recording those occurrences I wanted to preserve as soon as I could get to a private place. In each hospital I was given an office, to which I returned repeatedly during the day to write down more extensive records and dictate memos to myself. Only on rare occasions were interviews of a structured nature held, and those few which were necessary involved personnel from whom I wanted to gather technical information about hospital procedures. Some of these interviews were recorded, and some of the information gathered through them appears in succeeding chapters.

On various occasions, unsuccessful attempts were made to record actual conversations. With the permission of administrators, tape recorders were placed in concealed locations, and wireless transmitters were carried on my body. However, due to the high level of background noise in the hospital setting, only bits and pieces of conversational sequences were transcribed. In the body of the text wherever double quotation marks are used to frame a person's speech, or indentations are made to indicate a quotation, the quotation is as nearly literal as on-the-spot hand-written recording will permit. My limited ability with shorthand transcribing aided somewhat in this recording activity.

In doing field work, investigating "death," I have been aware of the possible effect of my own presence on the behavior of participants on the scene, and my only claim to its minimal relevance is my feeling that because of my long stay in the hospital, particularly at County, staff came to take my presence for granted. While in the early days of my research at County I distinctly felt that, in many cases, staff members monitored their activities to show me what they thought I would want to see, as I became well known to staff and they less suspect of my intentions, I felt sufficiently disregarded to be relatively secure that what I was witnessing would have gone on were I not around.

Most of my information is based on casual conversations I had with members of the staff and, more importantly, on my observations on the scene. Each day I accompanied members of the house staff on the morning rounds, engaged them in conversation, and attended their conferences. On special days during the week I attended various specialty conferences, e.g., vascular surgery, cancer clinic, obstetrics rounds, etc. During the rest of my day I spent most of my time standing about nurses' stations, overhearing conversations in corridors, following physicians as they treated their patients, witnessing surgical, obstetrics, and autopsy procedures, sitting in waiting rooms and cafeterias, chatting with members of families, and the like. In both settings I was free to go where I pleased—and in County that included every corner of the hospital, from the morgue to the staff dining room. I had, in each setting, persons who might be considered as "informants," namely those with whom I had developed friendships and who, in conversation, supplied me with much information about their circumstances of work, technical matters, feelings about the institution, the practices of others, and information about happenings which took place when I was not present. In nearly every setting in which I spent time, I managed to befriend some worker and in conversation with him gain access to some of that setting's hidden features. On occasion, I was treated with what was from my standpoint a bit too much enthusiasm. At County, several interns, fresh out of medical school and anxious to demonstrate their grasp on the world of biophysical fact, gave me long lectures on the structure of the human organism, complete with live bedside demonstrations, some of them going so far as to insist that I "feel this," "press here," "put your hand over there." Occasionally my aid was enlisted to assist in a particular procedure by passing an instrument, helping prop up a patient, tighten a tourniquet, and the like, all of which I did to make myself as much a part of the scene as possible. I felt that by helping the morgue attendant transfer a dead patient from the bed to the stretcher, I made him feel as though his actions were not being so distantly observed as when I stood in the background and silently watched him at work. (It is perhaps of some methodological interest that young interns, particularly, regarded my project as having to do with technical aspects of dying and death. They saw me as some sort of a medical investigator.)

❦ ❦ ❦ THE PROBLEM OF THE STUDY

A central theoretical and methodological perspective guides much of the study to follow. That perspective says that the categories of hospital life, e.g., "life," "illness," "patient," "dying," "death," or whatever, are to be seen as *constituted by the practices of hospital personnel* as they engage in their daily routinized interactions within an organizational milieu. This perspective implies a special concern with the form a definition should take, that concern involving a search for the *procedural basis* of events. By this I mean that a search is made, via the ethnographic description of hospital social structure and activities, for those practices which give "death related categories" their concrete organizational foundations. Rather than entering the hospital to investigate "death" and "dying" as I conceived them, I sought to develop "definitions" of such phenomena based on actions involved in their recognition, treatment, and consequences. "Death" and "dying" *are*, from this perspective, the set of practices enforced when staff employ those terms in the course of their work day on the hospital ward. These practices involve ways of inspecting a body, of admitting and discharging a "patient," various consequent activities of regarding that body in one way or another, the kinds of judgmental considerations made by the examining physician and his staff, and a host of other decisional and administrative practices. Taken together, I refer to these practices as what "death" and "dying" *are*, not as the "ways dying and dead people are treated," or such a formulation. The practices of inspection, examination, disposition, announcing, pronouncing, discharging, wrapping, etc., that I shall explore below, collectively comprise what could be called the "parent" activity: "making a dead or dying person." My emphasis is on the "production of dying and death" (particularly in Chapter 4), and on the "production of a bereaved person" (particularly in Chapter 5).

This emphasis on events as constituted by socially organized actions or procedures is specifically designed to delineate the cultural components of the phenomena in question. In taking such a view, focussing on "natural states" as the products of organizationally prescribed, practical decision-making, I intend to discover the social character of these natural states. This is not to suggest that such natural states are not as well the products of the biological apparatus; of course they are. But biological "happenings" are "discovered," "recognized," "named," and "treated"—and these activities occur in an organized social world— by persons who have established rules of certification allowing certain of them to make officially valid designations, who premise institution- alized courses of action on the basis of their knowledge of their own and others' states. In fact, the very recognition and naming of such biologically locatable events as "death" occur as social activities: social in that they require special achieved competence, in that the propriety of the names given is determined by a cultural tradition, in that the correctness or incorrectness of a designation is a matter of immense practical concern to others.[8] These relevances give the categories "dying" and "death" a distinctly social basis; the very determinations that a person is "dead" or not, or "dying" or not, are socially infused activities. I shall argue that a separation of the social and biological components of these phenomena is difficult to achieve with any clarity.

This study thus seeks to explore the sociological structure of certain categories pertaining to death. Its foremost concern is not with such an interest as "attitudes toward death," but with the activities of "seeing death," "announcing death," "suspecting death," and the like, where in each case the ways in which these activities occur can be seen to furnish us the basis for a description of what death is as a sociological phe- nomenon. I warrant the entry of the sociologist into the medical world, not insofar as he can furnish the physician or nurse with information about social organization and social structure, but because that world is as much social, from its hierarchically organized status relations down to the activity of looking into a microscope and announcing a finding, as is any other domain of collective human activity. I hope to show the relevance of a sociological perspective for the description of even that hardest and coldest of biological facts—death. Particularly, I hope to do so without specifically performing transformations on the object, without focussing on its "sociological aspects" (e.g., the study of its effects on group structure or the like). Rather, I seek to show by examin- ing the phenomena of "dying" and "death" as physicians and nurses themselves regard them that such phenomena cannot be adequately described at any level without consulting the socially organized character

[8] The focus on practical actions, procedural definitions, and common sense knowledge derives from the ground-breaking work of Harold Garfinkel of UCLA. For ex- tensive considerations of common sense methods of categorization see especially his "Studies in the Routine Grounds of Everyday Activities," *Social Problems*, 11, No. 3 (Winter, 1964), 235–250, and his "Common Sense Knowledge of Social Structures," *Transactions of the Fourth World Congress of Sociology*, Milan, 1959, Volume 4, pp. 51–65. A volume of Professor Garfinkel's theoretical essays and empirical re- searches is currently in preparation for publication by Prentice-Hall, and a col- lection of articles by participants in his conferences on ethnomethodology at UCLA will be published shortly by Aldine Publishing Co.

of those judgmental activities and administrative considerations which are involved and eventuate in their discovery, treatment, and consequent effects.

In the course of my research a series of special topics came to interest me, and I have tried to incorporate discussions of them within the general theme of the study. In Chapter 3 I have included a discussion of some of the special problems of the morgue attendant, that person in the hospital most continuously involved in the grossest aspects of "death work." Some of the problems he experienced in his work are shared by those members of the society who, by virtue of the kind of work they do, find themselves continually seen as "on the job." With a very limited degree of flexibility, what they are up to is always available for others to see or infer, and as a consequence their work life is characterized by special sorts of pressures. My discussion of some of the morgue attendant's problems is intended as an essay in the sociology of occupations.

In the course of investigating deaths throughout the hospital, I became intrigued by the special problems that plague hospital staff and administrators and constitute a recurrent topic of many theological considerations, namely those surrounding the treatment of premature and younger fetus deaths. While much more can be said about this area, its legal, social, and administrative aspects, and while there is a particularly interesting investigation yet to be made into the structure of "bereavement" in the case of such deaths, I have restricted my attention here to matters that accord with the general theme of the study: namely, how decisions concerning death are made within the constraints of organizationally conceived necessities.

Within the general framework of the study's theme, "death as a procedurally conceived matter," I have sought to retain a general ethnographic stance in the discussion, keeping uppermost the concern to provide a documentation of facts of hospital life and death hitherto either unseen or unnoticed by outsiders. I feel it a shortcoming of research on hospital social organization that, with very few exceptions, no detailed accounting of patient care practices is available. Whatever work is available on "death in the hospital" is generally based on field interviews, rather removed from actual instances of dying, relying heavily on the use of informants who retrospectively report upon their attitudes and happenings at the time of the death. Whatever contribution this study might make as an addition to that research will hopefully derive from the fact that the information it contains was gained firsthand.

In Chapter 5 a different concern is discussed, one somewhat removed from the main subject matter of the early chapters. In the course of my observations, and particularly on the Emergency Unit of County,

I frequently had the opportunity to witness encounters between physicians and the relatives of recently deceased patients. Dressed as a physician, I entered the room with the doctor when he announced the person's death, remained silent throughout the encounter, and left with him. It is my suspicion that I was taken, by members of the family, to be "just another doctor." On the basis of the information about these encounters that I obtained in person, as well as that obtained from listening in on telephone call announcements of deaths (several physicians arranged to notify me when they planned to make such a phone call and allowed me use of an extension telephone), I have developed an analysis of what I regard as a central sociological feature of such occasions: the institutionalization of a conversational format of discourse as a means of transforming the occasion from one of trauma to a state where both physician and relative can sustain the proprieties of social interaction. On the basis of my observations in this setting, I have made suggestions concerning what I take to be some prominent problems of interaction between bereaved and nonbereaved persons in our society. That discussion is prefaced by an analysis of some of the organizational constraints operative in the release of bad news within the hospital.

While at Cohen, I had the opportunity to get to know several members of families of recently deceased patients, who were kind enough, in their state of emotional upset, to allow me to tag along with them as they left the hospital and went home. I managed to gain their confidence, discuss their problems with them, and, particularly, to observe the fashion in which they announced the death of their relative to others in the community. Only a limited number of such observations were made, and no firm basis for a descriptive analysis of their problems existed. Several general features of their behavior seemed to deserve comment, if only as a speculative first effort. In Chapter 6 I have presented what I feel to be some of the principles that appear most relevant in the dissemination of news of a death. In an area of inquiry so completely neglected, I felt that some comment, even based upon scanty information, was better than avoidance. The study of bereavement and postdeath patterns of interaction is sadly in need of concrete research, and while difficulties of observational access to such a domain may be great, they do not seem, at least on the basis of my experience, insurmountable. Hopefully I have provided, in that discussion, a basis for formulating more systematic inquiry in this area.

TWO

The Setting
of the County Hospital

❧❧❧ COUNTY HOSPITAL is a 440-bed, acute treatment, general hospital for the "indigent." It is incorporated within a county-wide medical care welfare system which in addition to County itself includes a long-term chronic care facility and a number of outpatient clinics. Both hospitals in the system, as well as the various outpatient clinics (the newest and largest of which is adjacent and attached to County) serve as training institutions for interns and residents. The system has no direct medical school affiliation. County is located in a lower-middle-class, foothill area of a large West Coast city, within an extensive metropolitan community composed of several large municipalities. The population of the city within which County is located has a rather sizeable and somewhat transient cohort of recently immigrant Southern Negroes, who reside in the city's extensive slum district. The community has something of a reputation as the major western center for immigrating Negroes, considered by some as the "Chicago of the post-war era." It is the slum district's inhabitants who constitute County's core base patient population.

The hospital theoretically provides medical care, through its regular inpatient and outpatient divisions, for all "indigent" residents of the county. The fact of an "indigent" or "charity" hospital can be misleading however, in that the care it provides is rarely free. Once admitted to the hospital, a patient is interviewed by a county-employed,

13

hospital-based "eligibility worker," whose task it is to assess the approximate percentage of total care costs which the hospital administration feels it can warrantably charge the patient, on the basis, presumably, of his income. These eligibility workers, all of them women, are civil-service employees, whose main training consists in the acquisition of knowledge of local welfare regulations. While they report that only a small percentage of the patients, less than 25 per cent, ever pay their bills, rather consistent efforts are made, with the support of local law enforcement agencies, to collect as much as is feasible of the total assessed amount. Assessed bills have in many instances exceeded a thousand dollars, even in cases of patients whose chief sources of income are monthly welfare checks. In the past, wages and welfare checks have been garnished as a means of extracting payments for hospital costs. There is currently some controversy developing about the propriety of this practice, whereby two tax supported institutions—the welfare system and the health system—so thrive off one another, circulating the same monies. In recent years there has purportedly been somewhat less enthusiasm in the collection of payments than was reportedly exhibited in the 1950's.[1]

As a county institution, the hospital's legal affairs are handled by the county district attorney's office, which serves as its legal advisor in areas of forensic medicine and many matters of hospital policy. The collection of bills is the responsibility of county collection agencies, with proper assistance obtainable from the police department. While administered by a physician, ultimate say-so in many areas of fiscal and medical policy is in the hands of the county commissioner's office. Therefore, with a Catholic and influential district attorney, for example, such matters as the propriety of performing sterilization operations on women can be legitimately decided by the county commissioners; it is against hospital policy for an obstetrician to sever a woman's Fallopian tubes during surgery, even if he feels it medically advisable to do so and has the patient's permission.[2] The penalty for performing such an operation is immediate dismissal from the hospital, and at least one occasion is known where that penalty was invoked. An obstetrician re-

[1] "Charity" hospitals are known not to be free. For national figures on the percentage of hospital costs met by patients in such institutions, see J. H. Hayes and H. Becker, *Financing Hospital Care in the United States*, 3 vols. (New York: Blakiston, 1954), p. 52, and S. E. Harris, *The Economics of American Medicine* (New York: The Macmillan Company, 1964), pp. 229–237.

[2] The county is known to be rather conservative in its attitudes toward recipients of welfare. In recent years there has been a campaign, not without objection, to investigate females receiving welfare checks on the basis of nonsupport. Squads of "eligibility workers" have occasionally descended on the homes of such residents in predawn hours and if a man is found at the residence, welfare payments are discontinued and, on not a few occasions, criminal prosecutions on "welfare fraud" statutes are initiated.

ported, "I've held those tubes in my hands many times during a C-Section and heard the woman beg me to cut them, but I can't do it, even if she's had a dozen kids." The County obstetrician is obliged to refer such cases to private physicians who practice in hospitals where such procedures are permissible. This includes nearly all local facilities except County (and is typically something which such a patient cannot afford). Several years ago there reportedly was a heated controversy over the ethicality of performing hysterectomies on patients. The commissioner's office, under the persuasion of the district attorney, was said to have sought to convince hospital administrators to refer all cases of needed surgery in that area to other hospitals, but hospital administrators argued that such a practice would constitute neglect of medical responsibility. A ruling that the operating surgeon must obtain written permission from the medical director of the hospital and two consulting physicians before such surgery apparently resolved the issue.

In the daily course of medical practice at County, interference with policy from county officials is held to a minimum, and the bureaucracy is routinely circumvented by house staff who engage in minor violations of legal regulations. So, for example, the requirement to obtain signatures prior to an hysterectomy has been treated lightly, often without any actual consultation on the case. On several occasions, the signatures of colleagues were signed on the basis of telephone conversation permission. The hospital staff member is theoretically obligated to report to proper authorities any crimes he learns of or has reason to believe might have occurred. The confidentiality of the doctor-patient relationship is thereby somewhat weakened; yet, County physicians do not regularly report upon the criminal activities they know of, or suspect, if not so much because of an ideological commitment not to do so, then because of the bureaucratic paper work and time involved. In the Emergency Ward, a distinct branch of the main hospital, many "walk-ins" occur, i.e., persons who arrive at the division on their own accord, without ambulance or police delivery. Some of these persons have been the object of physical attack, or suffer injuries or diseases as a result of behavior which might be considered as adequate grounds for prosecution. It is primarily when hospital physicians believe that the police are or will become involved in the case and that they themselves will be held to account for not reporting their own involvement in it that police headquarters is notified. Physicians treat many drunks, attempted suicides, and the like without informing the police that these people are in their custody. While it is officially required that the names of all women known to be delivering illegitimately conceived children be submitted to proper authorities (because of the controls these authorities can exercise over such matters as welfare assistance checks), these names are rarely submitted (approximately 40 per cent of the births at County are of illegitimately conceived infants). In some instances operating obstetricians have been known to sever Fallopian tubes at the request of their patients, particularly if they have assurances that the patient will not have cause in the future to register a complaint. One physician reported that he was waiting until just before his residency was completed and that he would then try to convince women who had had very large numbers of children to allow him to "tie their tubes."

Generally, despite its status as a county agency in a county well-known for its punitive attitude toward recipients of welfare, the hospital is a relatively safe place to be treated, from the standpoint of possible discovery and prosecution for illegal behavior. Knowledge of "major" crimes will be transmitted, but many "minor" ones go officially unnoticed. In the Emergency Unit there is a designation "50–50," a code term for all police cases. When a person is treated who has committed an offense and is so termed, a special form is to be filled out and, in some cases, the police department notified. In most cases, drunks are treated and no report issued. In matters such as fist fights, if no weapons have been used, a report will generally not be made. If, however, a patient should treat the physician with what is regarded as disrespect, a report may be issued, and the threat of such an action has been used, by physicians in this unit, to subdue persons who are "recalcitrant." In cases of attempted suicide, there seems to be some variation in reporting depending upon the particular physician in charge and the severity of the attempt. In those cases which the attending physician considers to warrant psychiatric intervention, the police are notified and a "temporary hold" placed on the patient. With a policeman's signature, the person can be restrained in the hospital's psychiatric ward for a period of 72 hours, and if further action is taken he can be brought before a commitment hearing (there is a small courtroom on the psychiatric ward where, several times a week, a county superior court judge hears commitment proceedings). In some potential suicide cases, and particularly if the attending physician holds a negative attitude about this course of action, a patient will be released after treatment with no police report. This is especially likely if the physician regards the attempt as "insincere," a decision which is generally reached if the physical consequences of the attempt were negligible, e.g., the patient ingested a half-dozen sleeping pills and remained conscious throughout. Such cases are considered as "fakes" and such patients frequently released.

There are some areas of tension between county officials and hospital personnel regarding the proper role of the hospital as a county-affiliated institution. The major one involves the Emergency Unit, where most "criminals" are treated and victims of violence patched up. Staff have claimed that local police officials favor the use of Emergency Unit facilities as relatively safe places to coerce and beat criminal suspects. There is a small office in the ward that is directly in view of the public waiting room, designated as a "Press Room," to which suspects are taken by police when blood tests for alcoholism are done (the staff of the ward is responsible for giving such tests on a policeman's request). On several occasions police have been known to bring suspects there and, so it would appear from the noise that issues from that room, beat them. While the police are apparently not troubled about what they must know people overhear while they are in the room, on numerous occasions rather harsh words have been exchanged between them and nursing and medical personnel who maintain that the room is being improperly used. During a period of nine months several formal protests were made by the hospital to the police department, but at the end of that period, such "beatings" were still being heard, particularly on Saturday nights. A nurse commented: "The cops wouldn't dare do that (beat suspects) on the streets where they could be seen, so they come in here where they think no one will say anything." The Emergency Ward has two holding cells, much like prison cells, where criminal suspects receiving medical treatment who require overnight care are kept during their transit from the street to prison. This facility is a distinctive mark of the County Hospital, along with the appearance of large numbers of policemen in the Emergency Ward on busy weekend evenings. When police officers accompany prisoners to the hospital for treatment, they have the legal duty to stay with their prisoners while they are seen by a physician. It is common in the Emergency Ward to find policemen restraining alcoholic and epileptic prisoners while they are being examined and treated by the attending physician. On such occasions, nurses, who would normally assist in treating such patients, are often relieved by policemen, who are sometimes less than totally mindful of the physiological effects of the way in which they employ restraints. On several occasions, a particular surgical resident refused to examine "police patients" because of the ways they were handled by police. Generally, however, nurses leave the room and doctors quietly treat the policeman's charge. Some physicians often page for a policeman to come into a treatment room and aid in subduing an alcoholic patient who is "causing trouble." On several nights there were fist fights in the treatment rooms; in one case a policeman hit a man who was cursing him while being bandaged for facial lacerations by a physician.

The main part of the hospital is devoid of obvious signs of official connection with county government agencies, though in its over-all appearance resembles many such tax-supported institutions, particularly the traditional American county or city hospital. The physical plant is something of an eyesore. The grayish-brown building sprawls rather haphazardly along the edge of a hillside, bounded by large walls and moderately busy streets. To reach the main entrance from the street, one has to climb what appear as an infinite number of steps, up a rather steep incline. The surrounding residential neighborhood is a transitional area of old, deteriorating wooden houses, occasionally interspersed with newer duplex-type apartment buildings. Architecturally, the hospital could be said to be early twentieth-century "American Gothic." Its hallways are dingy, poorly lit, and badly ventilated. The building has no visitors' eating facilities, with the exception of a few old vending machines, which are typically out of order; the gift shop which is commonly found in middle-class hospitals is, congruent with other facts about County, absent. A newcomer quickly detects a range of rather obnoxious odors, more noisome than usually encountered in the public parts of most hospitals, which add to the generally depressing mood of the setting. The only relatively bright spots in the building are those places which are set aside for use by the medical and nursing staff, e.g., lounges, cafeterias, offices, etc., and the new clinic building, adjoined to the main plant by a long and airy corridor. There are gardens surrounding the building, all of which are carefully planted and groomed, and seldom used. In its overall physical structure, the hospital appears considerably delapidated.[3]

The main plant consists of a long narrow building, four floors high. On each floor there is a long, wide corridor, off which branch four wings of patients' beds. Altogether there are sixteen such wings, stacked on top of each other, four per floor. The wing on each floor is referred to as a "ward," each separately designated for a different medical or surgical service. The hospital has the usual range of divisions, e.g., medicine, surgery, obstetrics, pediatrics, orthopedics, etc., but not the more specialized services often found in research-oriented and wealthier institutions —neurology, cancer ward, ophthamology, audiology, cardiology, and the like. On the medical wards, diseases from diabetes to cancer to glaucoma to syphilis will be found, and patients with quite dissimilar medical problems often are assigned to the same rooms.

Although called "wards," the wings differ from what typically goes by this term. Each ward is an arm of the central corridor and consists of a series of private, semiprivate, four-, six-, and eight-bed rooms, the latter of which have the more traditional character of wards, This ward is unofficially divided into two sections, that half closest to the central corridor (which is perpendicular to the ward corridor) being re-

[3] For an excellent description of a hospital with very many physical features similar to County, see Jan De Hartog's account of a Houston, Texas, general hospital in *The Hospital* (New York: Atheneum Publishers, 1964).

served for the more seriously ill patients, the outside half, farthest from the main corridor, for the ambulatory and semi-ambulatory patients. A nurses' station constitutes the division between the two sections, and adjacent to it are a supply room, sterilization room, examination room, and small laboratory. The larger ward rooms—six and eight beds each— are in the "ambulatory section," and the private, semiprivate, and four-bed rooms, in the "critically ill" half. Each of the sixteen hospital wards is identical in these respects. At the main corridor end of the ward is an old elevator, officially designated for hospital staff only, though not always used by them alone. There are large elevators in the central part of the hospital, where the main corridor joins the corridor to the clinic building, and where administrative offices, operating rooms, and cafeterias for employees are located. These elevators are marked for visitors' use. Unlike the layout at some hospitals, such as Cohen, all elevators in County are visible to visitors, and closely enough visible so that what is being transported from floor to floor, including dead bodies, can be seen by a properly situated onlooker. Over-all, the hospital is not structured to provide distinctly public and nonpublic places, with the exception of the operating room area, the maternity ward, the premature nursery, and the hospital morgue.

Each ward corridor is about 75 feet long and 10 feet wide; the main corridor, which runs the entire length of the hospital, is considerably wider. The private and semiprivate rooms are quite tiny by most contemporary hospital standards. Aside from the bed, there is a single wooden chair and small wooden nightstand per patient; the overhead room light supplies the only illumination, for there are no individual bed lights. The private room is about 8 by 10 feet in dimension, the semiprivate room about 10 by 15. While apparently clean and freshly painted, the ward and rooms are very drab and poorly ventilated. There are no visitors' waiting rooms on the ward itself; the only place a visitor can await the beginning of visiting hours is in the general hospital lobby, at the front of the building, which, with its long benches, resembles a train station. If, during a visit with a patient, a relative is asked to leave the room, he must stand in the ward corridor. None of the doors to individual rooms is closed, with an exception to be described below, so that a visitor can witness nearly everything that goes on in neighboring rooms. While curtains surround each bed in the multi-bed rooms, they are not always drawn at appropriate times. During visiting hours, as one walks down the hall to a patient's room, he is quite likely to see several patients' bodies exposed as bed clothes are changed or examinations conducted. Except on certain occasions, the use of curtains to screen off a bed is only a gesture, so that there is nearly always

a degree of openness of the screen, with consequent visibility for an onlooker.[4]

"Security measures" at County are noticeably less extensive than at
Cohen. While there are considerably fewer visitors around the hospital
than is the case at Cohen, restrictions on their freedom of movement are
not very great. On the obstetrics ward at Cohen, when the "babies are
out," i.e., when infants are being taken to their mothers for feeding, a
nurse stands guard at the elevator to prohibit the entry on the floor of
unauthorized people, which includes, in addition to visitors, all hospital
personnel who have no rightful business on the maternity floor. The
restriction applies to physicians who have no patients on the floor. At
County Hospital, the infant nursery is on a different floor from the
maternity patients' beds, and babies are brought up in the elevator,
carried by student nurses, when feeding time approaches. While some
effort is made to insure that the elevator will be empty, on numerous occasions I saw persons other than nurses riding along, e.g., janitors, visitors,
physicians, etc. When this was related to OB personnel at Cohen, they
expressed shock at the implied lack of concern with asepsis. When
mothers nurse their infants at Cohen, curtains are drawn between their
beds in multibed rooms to afford privacy and presumably limit the
possibilities of germ spread from one mother to another's child.

At County, an interesting method of child-feeding is characteristic
of certain general features of that hospital's atmosphere. At appointed
hours during the day, the student nurses depart, en masse, from where
they are working and go to "pick up babies" from the nursery. At a coordinated moment, an OB nurse rings a loud buzzer to tell the recuperat-
ing mothers that it is feeding time, whereupon the mothers, in their
characteristic postdelivery shuffle, form a rough line in the corridor and
painfully meander down the hall to a large "feeding room." In this feeding
room are a dozen or so old rocking chairs, set about in a cozy circle,
where the mothers sit, prepare their breasts for feeding, and await the
arrival of the nurses' brigade. Those mothers who are not breast-feeding
their babies (and the proportion of them is very low at County and quite
high at Cohen) are provided with prepared formula bottles. Apparently,
public feeding would be an intolerable practice at modest middle-class
institutions where, at least as in the case of Cohen, privacy at feeding
time is cherished and infringements upon it negatively sanctioned. (The
fact that the investigator was freely permitted to observe the mass-feeding
practice at County, yet treated much as a visitor at feeding time at Cohen,

[4] I found this to be true as I walked down ward corridors through areas where it was
proper for visitors to be, though it is not altogether clear that among County's patient
and relative population such visibility would be a noticeable matter. It may be a feature striking only to middle-class eyes.

is partially indicative of the general ideological difference between the two settings in this regard.)

Throughout County, many aspects of medical care are carried out on a mass basis. Most X-ray examinations are done in the morning hours, when the doctors' orders from the previous day are consulted to prepare those patients for X ray whose examination has been requested. While at Cohen patients are individually taken to X ray, at County several are taken at one time, by a group of attendants. There is a morning line-up of stretchers and after all patients scheduled for radiological examinations have been assembled, a group of attendants march them off together. If only one patient is scheduled for an X ray, and there is no urgency attached to the request, it would not be considered especially improper for a nurse to hold up sending him to X ray until other similar examinations were ordered. For example, if a doctor left orders for a patient to have an X ray, that patient might not have an X ray for two days, until several other X-ray exams were called for. It is not improper to employ a rationale that says: "There's no use having an attendant removed from other work just to take one patient over to X ray." Similarly, laboratory tests are ordered in batches, rather than on a one-by-one basis. If a physician has to do a pelvic examination he will go through the charts to see if any other such examinations are needed, and if so, try to do them all at the same time, one after the other. For a certain range of tasks, like taking blood pressures, temperatures, and pulse readings, there is a tendency at all hospitals to schedule such activities by the clock, and to do them for all patients at the same time each day. At County, one finds similar scheduling for the sorts of activities, which, at Cohen, would not be so scheduled. Examples are: doing pelvic examinations in OB, doing spinal taps, ordering medications for patients, taking patients to X ray, etc. At Cohen, nearly every ward has its own EKG (electrocardiogram) machine. At County, there are a limited number of such machines and the administration of EKG examinations follows a routine. A woman technician spends her entire day systematically wheeling an EKG machine through the hospital's wards; she checks the charts on each ward and does EKG's on all patients for whom they are ordered. If a physician orders an EKG, he must wait for the technician's round to bring her to his ward. In Emergency Ward routine, EKG machines are available for case-by-case use, but elsewhere in the hospital one places an order and awaits the arrival of the machine. In many respects, the County patient is at the mercy of the scheduled character of medical care activities; at Cohen such schedules are so frequently violated by physicians' requests to "have it done now," that the request, rather than the schedule, is the basis for administering treatments.

The feasibility of mass treatment based on routine is enhanced by the fact that at County there are no private patients. Physicians treat a bank of patients, the central principle for the allocation of work being ecological, i.e., the physician mans a ward and treats its patients. This fact has several rather important consequences that will be discussed shortly and referred to repeatedly in the course of later chapters. First, a few words about the character of the medical staff.

The chief sense in which County is a "county hospital" seems to lie in the fact that no private patients are treated there. While a given patient might have a private physician, should that person be admitted to County, his own physician can no longer treat him. Referrals to County by private physicians are rather infrequently made and typically only if hospital care is considered quite essential and the patient has no funds. All patients are the patients of the hospital's employed intern and resident physicians. In hospital terminology, County's staff is strictly a "house staff." These doctors are under the general supervision of a county-salaried medical director, the chief administrator of the hospital, and assume full responsibility for the admission, treatment, and discharge of all patients.

The medical staff consists of approximately 45 interns, 30 residents, and a dozen part-time division directors. The actual number of physicians in the house at any one time, and from year to year, varies slightly depending upon the hospital's success in recruiting new interns and residents. In recent years the number of applications for internships and residencies has been roughly equal to the number of positions available, so that nearly all applicants are accepted. Private physicians are appointed, with token salaries, to posts as the "directors" of various hospital services, and their central responsibility is to make "grand medical rounds" each week with the permanent house staff. They do not treat patients directly, nor may they admit their own patients to the hospital. They are essentially consultants, with a very limited voice in matters of general hospital and medical policy. Unlike the "private physician" at Cohen Hospital, they have no final word in the treatment decisions on any given case, that authority resting with the chief resident of the service. In addition to these nominal directors of services, a group of private physicians rotates through the hospital, one month each per year, offering free consultative "charity" service. During his month of service a private physician comes to the hospital twice a week, in the mornings, and makes daily rounds with the house staff, providing general consultative advice. He has no authority in planning treatment, that authority residing solely with the house staff, within which the intern is answerable to the resident, the resident to the chief resident, and the chief resident to the medical director. While at Cohen the visiting man is a key figure (and not really a "visitor" insofar as nearly all of his hospitalized patients are at Cohen and he often spends a considerable part of his day there), at County the visiting man is a true "visitor," with very limited say-so. He is, in his presence, accorded polite deference and, behind his back regarded as something of an intruder. Interactions between house staff and "visiting men" have the character of "going through the motions," and this seems to be recognized by both parties. At Cohen Hospital, a resident is often obliged to "have a consult" on a "service" patient (a patient who has no private physician), meaning that he is obliged to seek the advice of a visiting man before instituting treatment, and the decision of the visiting man is binding. At County, the only people with such authority are the residents. A resident at Cohen who was having difficulty locating his "consult" and was thereby held up in his treatment of a patient (and made to stay on after his shift was over) complained, "Oh, for the good old days of the county hospital where we didn't have to go through this nonsense."

The resident and intern physicians at County are drawn primarily from the state university medical schools, and among these, the average quality schools. Of the 45 interns, some 30 came from schools such as the Universities of Iowa, Nebraska, Oregon, Washington, California, Utah, North Carolina, Tennessee, Wisconsin, Michigan, Alabama, Indiana, and Georgia. A few came from smaller colleges of lesser repute; none was a graduate of the bigger and better known medical schools such as Chicago, Harvard, Yale, Stanford, Kansas, Washington University, Johns Hopkins, and Columbia. From what can be gathered from conversation with hospital administrators, most of the interns were in the second quarter of their graduating classes, i.e., between the fiftieth and seventy-fifth percentiles. County therefore seems to get better than average but not top-notch students from fairly respectable state university medical schools. Many of the residents did their internships at County (approximately 60 per cent); some came from other comparable hospitals in the United States; none from hospitals which would generally be considered as better quality institutions. When asked informally about the reasons they had chosen County, interns reported that they wanted to work in a county hospital where one gets 'more experience,' and, as a prominent reason, many said they wanted to come to the West Coast in order eventually to practice medicine there. Quite a few interns expressed disappointment with the West Coast, complaining that while they had expected beaches, night clubs, and women, they had found instead that they were living in a transitional slum area of a city where recreational facilities were not extensive. The relatively high proportion of interns who stay on at County seems partially explainable by the difficulty County interns have in getting residency posts in other institutions.[5]

As a hospital with no visiting staff, i.e., no private physicians treating private patients, greater responsibility is given to intern and resident physicians. In the private hospital, an internship is very often rightly regarded as involving quite menial, nonresponsible work. At County, however, interns are given responsibility to engage in those kinds of medical activities which, in private hospitals, would be performed only by residents. Likewise, residents are granted much less freedom of movement and responsibility for independent decision-making in the private hospital than at County. All through the staff hierarchy, we find a generally greater amount of responsibility independently assumed by personnel than would be assumed by similarly stationed personnel in a private hospital. Several examples can be given: At County, nearly all babies are delivered by interns and residents, and nurses assist in deliveries by giving anesthesia, when necessary. At Cohen Hospital, all deliveries are performed by private physicians or residents, and the latter only on "service patients." At County, first-year residents often assume complete charge of relatively routine but major surgical procedures, e.g., appendectomies. The intern assists with suturing. At Cohen Hospital, first-year residents never make incisions and interns are never allowed to do suturing, those tasks being allotted to the advanced resident and junior resident respectively. At Cohen, the student nurse is generally not allowed to start an intraveneous injection to prepare for IV feeding; at County, an intern would consider it beneath him to be asked to start an IV, and oftentimes so would a nurse, who would call upon a student. Some IV solutions are administered through what is known as a "cutdown." Here, in part because of the potency of the solution being administered and the concern not to have that solution invade surrounding tissue, a small incision is made, typically in the leg, a vein is located, severed, and affixed to the IV needle to permit sure entry of the medicine directly into the blood stream. At County, interns regularly do cutdowns, in fact residents have been known to call upon interns to do them. At Cohen, interns are not permitted to perform the procedure, but only to assist the resident, who does the major work.

Generally, the absence of the private physician lowers the upper level of authority and upgrades the domains of responsibility at all staff levels. A newcomer to County gets the initial and perhaps lasting

---

[5] For general discussions of recruitment to internships and data on the location of medical students after graduation, see W. Glaser, "Internship Appointments of Medical Students," *Administrative Science Quarterly*, 4 (December, 1959), 337–356, and J. E. Deitrick and R. C. Berson, *Medical Schools in the United States at Mid-Century* (New York: The Macmillan Company, 1953), Chapter 14.

impression of a hospital "run by boys," where it is at first quite incongruous (perhaps only to the middle-class observer) to see quite young men delivering babies, doing surgery, and the like. The traditional image of the physician, whose countenance and bedside manner convey experience, is as markedly absent at County as it is present at Cohen. The average age of the County physician is 28, that of the Cohen doctor in the forties.

The absence of the practicing, experienced specialist that one finds in the key authority position in many university-affiliated hospitals and in private institutions generally, provides a special character both to the kind of "learning" one does at County and to the kind of medicine and surgery practiced there. At County, residents and interns learn almost exclusively from each other. There is no outside source of knowledge and experience except that of the textbook and the extremely nonsystematic instruction provided, on a very occasional basis, by the "visiting man." The intern learns from the resident and the resident from other residents. Knowledge is thus "internally generated," as it comes *down* from residents and not *in* from established professional physicians. Whatever experience the most experienced and knowledgeable physician in the hospital has, he has achieved in working at the hospital and not via consultation or instruction from outside. In a rather strict sense, "County medicine" is just that, with the exception of those comparative influences which a diversity of medical school backgrounds might provide. In the world of medicine generally, consultation and supervision are institutionalized the way they are in part because they provide for diversity in training, exposure to wide varieties of medical experiences, etc. By upgrading the age of the person with the "final word," the hospital where the private specialist physician has great power seeks to insure a broad base of experience for diagnostic and treatment effectiveness. At County, the internal generation of knowledge, without substantial external supplement by those with greater experience, makes it appropriate for one to regard the setting as a "closed system," in an information, or more generally, ideological sense. County's teachers are its own students, and this "familial" character tends to be a limiting feature, in certain key respects. One major consequence is that innovation is drastically limited. The development of new techniques, dissemination of new information about drugs and disease properties, treatment programs, etc., occurs from within only, on the basis of experience at County alone, by County physicians alone. Over and above that basic store of knowledge that a medical school education provides, learning at County is largely a do-it-yourself matter, and the environment is, in many respects, an *experimental* one, in the practical rather than research sense of that term. A lack of daily contact with the ongoing outside world of medical practice

provides for a general technological stagnation. Many procedures which
have long since been abandoned in favor of more modern practices at
other hospitals are still much in vogue at County. The conservatism of
medical care is not so much a principled conservatism, based on a well-
experienced ideology, as a forced one. The relatively low budget for the
purchase of new equipment is only a partial explanation; the general
lack of contact with long-term experience seems quite important. Many
County physicians are aware of the cultural lag and recognize that the
sheer fact that its young men have been exposed to modern medical
school training is not sufficient a basis for innovation and change, but
that keeping pace with current developments best occurs once one has
left an internship and residency and begins actively to practice his specialty in interaction with colleagues.

In addition to the general innovative vacuum at County, certain
particular practices cannot be instituted without greater experience than
an internship or residency provides. For example, at many hospitals in the
United States, no one but a "boarded" obstetrician can use forceps in the
delivery of a newborn. There are many varieties of forceps, and their
proper use requires very experienced hands. The use of forceps is routine
in the delivery room at Cohen, but virtually nonexistent at County.
Cohen physicians use forceps in a great proportion of normal deliveries
and argue that rather than being dangerous, as lay persons often feel,
the proper use of forceps greatly expedites the delivery of a baby and is
often a safer procedure than allowing the head to exit the birth canal un-
assisted, at the risk of an overly long delivery with a consequent in-
crease in fetal difficulties. At County, a key reason for the absence of
forceps deliveries is that no one gets sufficient experience in conducting
the procedure. By the time one begins to have the prerequisite skills
necessary for learning to do difficult forceps deliveries, he has completed his residency and left the hospital to begin private practice.
The obstetrician gains most of his experience in forceps deliveries after
he has completed his residency and begins his specialty practice. The
same general problem is true of a wide variety of technical skills, and
in every such case there is no available knowledge base at the hospital
whose upper level of medically competent authority is constituted by the
house staff resident.

With no private patients in the hospital, the key method of patient
treatment is ecologically based. One treats not patients so much as one
does a "tour of duty." The clock and calendar govern the way the intern's
time is allocated—not the particular patients who happen to be his charge
for the day. Once he is "off duty," he relegates his care of the patient to
his colleague, and the latter does not feel obligated to consult the former
to get clearance for instituting a treatment, nor does the former feel

particularly obligated to retain any control in the patient's care. While a wide degree of latitude is given younger personnel as regards their rights to perform complicated procedures, perhaps "responsibility" is not an appropriate term, for the County physician's obligations are not as closely controlled as the Cohen physician's, who is answerable at many points to a formidable collection of superiors. It is important to note, for our later discussion will return to the matter, that one of the main differences between being a physician at County and at Cohen derives from the fact that given the lack of an historical development and involvement with relatives and patients, County doctors can interchange with one another in the performance of a wide range of tasks. Once a history between physician and relative and physician and patient has become well-established, and a traditional "doctor-patient-relative" contractual understanding reached, a certain segment of the doctor's tasks can no longer be relegated or delegated to other doctors to perform. At County Hospital, the delegation of tasks is quite common, and extends to those kinds of tasks which, at Cohen, would not be properly delegateable, e.g., talking to the family about the patient's condition, doing surgery, etc. It can be noted parenthetically that one of the key worries some persons have about "socialized" medicine derives from the possibility that such arrangements will militate against the development of a continuous doctor-patient relationship and thus allow for relatively uncontrolled interchangeability of physicians. Of course this constitutes, at the same time, one of the central freedoms of such arrangements for physicians, although one which, apparently, is not of great enough import to stand as a good reason for such arrangements.[6]

The County physician finds that his attachments are a thing of the moment, and that at any point in the day, by virtue of the fact that he is an employee of the hospital and not a "visitor with a patient," he may find himself suddenly thrust into the midst of a case, the beginning and end of which he has never and will never have a part in. The ward of the hospital is, from the County intern or resident's perspective, an environment of medical events, not persons, to a somewhat greater extent than seems to be the case with the physician in the private hospital. A commonly expressed feeling among County physicians is that private practice at least offers the advantage of being able to select one's patients; yet, at the same time, the interchangeability of physicians is valued by County physicians in part because it allows not getting involved with those patients who are regarded as less than desirable social types. I

[6] For an analysis of another organization wherein interchangeability of personnel and mass treatments were prominent work features, see D. Sudnow, "Normal Crimes: Sociological Features of the Penal Code in a Public Defender Office," *Social Problems*, **12**, No. 3 (Winter, 1965), 255–276.

shall have more to say about this "advantage" immediately below and in later chapters.

The "absence" of the visiting physician who spends much of his career practicing medicine in the same hospital gives County Hospital a rather special organizational quality. Every year there is a complete turn-over of the intern population, and every fourth year, of the entire medical staff. County's staff members (partially perhaps as a consequence of this turnover) have a limited degree of interest in the institution itself, re-garding it as a temporary field setting rather than an organization whose ideology, development, reputation, etc., affects and reflects their own. There is a characteristic attitude of indifference toward the setting. Doctors frequently talk negatively of the facilities and the patient popu-lation, not so much to indicate a desire for change, improvement, and the like, as to maintain a social distance from implicit identification with "this kind of medicine" and "this kind of patient." The practice developed in the Emergency Unit several years ago of keeping an informal digest of "funny" instances of Negro folk medicine knowledge and vocabularies, which physicians and nurses pick up in their interactions with patients. The dozen-or-so-page list is hung on the bulletin board in the doctors' office and is periodically consulted, during slack work hours, as a source of humor. It contains such references as "I's got a sore in my bagiva," "Ma die Betsies is actin' up," "I's had venal disease," etc.; each entry is carefully constructed to retain the phonetics of the purported Negro usage. Derogatory talk about patients is rather common, particularly about those patients whose behavior, way of life, etc., when regarded from a middle-class perspective, are considered morally obnoxious. A favored topic of conversation and gestural imitation is the alcoholic's be-havior; another recurrently noticed and talked about matter is the body odors of lower-class persons, some of which are regarded as particularly repulsive. Below, in my discussion of the care given "dying" patients in Chapter 4, I have occasion to consider the way physicians feel about such patients in more detail.

With a large turnover of essential personnel each year, County Hos-pital has a certain degree of instability. The incoming medical student doesn't have an already established medical order in which he shall be-come socialized and through which he shall progress. Rather, during the period of yearly turnover, there is something of a vacuum of order, as when an entire corporation or government suddenly changes hands. The key source of continuity during this change of staff is the nursing division, whose personnel constitute the only permanent people on the scene. While at Cohen the new medical staff member learns local culture from upper-echelon medical people, this is only partially so at County, where the nurse is regarded as a much more important person, one whom the physician can and must consult on a wide variety of organizational matters.

There is a characteristic period of relative chaos and conflict at the beginning of the new year when the incoming crop of interns arrives. Freed from the disciplines of medical school life, the new doctor seems to feel himself at last as one who gives orders and mobilizes the resources of the hospital in the care of his patient. A period of several weeks is considered necessary for the intern to learn to respect the wisdom of the nurse, on whom he must rely to learn almost everything he has to know to get along in County. He must learn to respect the fact that the hospital, despite the near absence of supervisory physicians, nonetheless has an order that was constructed without regard for him, in which he must "make it." The characteristic kind of tension involves giving orders. Inexperienced doctors abruptly order older nurses about, and nurses answer, "Get it yourself," disillusioning physicians about the scope of respect they will legitimately receive.

Interchangeability of tasks and greater responsibility in the care of patients are presumably among the reasons that make county hospitals good places to learn to practice medicine. Another reason is apparently the fact that in such institutions the general condition of the patients is quite poor. As an acute treatment hospital, County is a place which is entered, most typically, in cases of rather severe illness, where living at home has become impossible. A very large proportion of its patients enter the hospital via ambulance, through the Emergency Ward section. Very few are referred to the hospital by physicians, but come at the insistence of the family or on the basis of their own grasp of their need for care. While it is true that many patients use the County Hospital for reasons which would, among middle-class persons, warrant merely a visit to a doctor, these patients are not admitted to a hospital bed, but are treated in the Emergency Ward or referred to a clinic division.[7]

---

[7] It is not infrequent for a patient to arrive in an ambulance and complain of a cold; and it seems that lower-class Negroes, in particular, consider the possibility that because of various welfare assistance arrangements they won't have to pay for the ambulance or for the care they receive at the hospital. It is frequent, in the Emergency Unit, for persons who arrive not to have car fare home. There is a box of petty cash kept at the Unit desk which is used to pay cab fares for those who request it. How members of the community develop knowledge of the availability of such resources is a matter of some interest. The Emergency Unit apparently had a wide variety of uses, as was evidenced particularly one evening when a woman arrived at the Unit with a bandage wrapped about her head, which a physician had observed her to tie carefully as she left her car and approached the front doorway. Women arrive, frequently, at all hours of the night, with young children, and spend the night sitting up in the waiting room.

The use of ambulances has been noted by other observers. In Julius Horwitz's *The Inhabitants* (New York: Signet Books, 1960), p. 9, a building superintendent says:

> Sick! When I'm sick I think twice before I call a doctor. And these slobs
> are down here every ten minutes for me to call an ambulance. An ambu-

Those patients who are admitted to the hospital bed are thus quite ill. This is partially explainable by the fact that they delay seeking care for physical complaints, don't regularly see physicians, and are hence not advised to enter the hospital in the early stages of illness. It is also partially explainable by the fact that County turns away patients after finding that their conditions are not serious.[8] There is no "elective surgery" at County, i.e., the surgery done there is done because the house staff consider it necessary in the course of the current treatment of the patient. Various types of surgery are far more frequent at Cohen Hospital than at County; for example: herniorrhaphies (hernia repair surgery), hysterectomies, cholecystectomies (gall bladder removal), mastectomies (breast removals). Hernia and hysterectomy surgery are generally done under the circumstance of physical discomfort and not for specific illness treatment. Hernia complaints typically involve lower abdominal pain, with no interference with physical functioning, and this "corrective surgery" is often close to "cosmetic surgery" in its general import. At Cohen, many herniorrhaphies are done as "corrective repair surgery"; at County such procedures are typically performed only when some essential functioning has been impaired, e.g., when strangulation of a bowel occurs and the hernia repair is essential to life. Likewise, hysterectomies are very often electively contracted. At Cohen, this surgery is quite frequently done (and among its population of middle-class women, often fashionable), whereas at County, gynecological surgery is usually done only when organ functioning is impaired, e.g., when severe infection occurs from an ovarian cyst, or when cancerous tissue is located. Procedures like gall bladder and breast removals are typically instigated upon early detection of the need for them. Many gall bladder removals are "unnecessary," i.e., are done so as to prevent the possibility of a serious emergency condition, the likelihood of which is not always considered sufficiently high to warrant the procedure. Breast removals are done at the early detection of cancerous tissue. Once a breast cancer becomes extensive and metastasizes, removal

---

lance no less. In my old neighborhood the only time they dared to call for an ambulance was when the person was already dead. And the funny part is that the ambulances come now.

[8] This policy is partially based on the desire of administrators to provide a better training environment. A rapid turnover of acutely ill patients is considered more suited to the task of teaching than the situation of long-term illness. This has been an historically familiar policy:

The heavy demand for admission to the well-equipped infirmaries made it necessary for some system of selection of patients to be introduced. The medical superintendents were quite clear about the criteria they wanted to use. They wanted the acute sick. This was the type of patient they had been trained to care for in the teaching hospitals.

From B. Abel-Smith, *The Hospitals in England and Wales* (Cambridge: Harvard University Press, 1964), p. 205.

of the breast is no longer a preventive measure and may become, medically speaking, useless. Among Cohen's middle-class patient population,
early detection of breast tumors is much more likely than among County's
base-patient population, and mastectomies are done many times a week.

The over-all character of medical and surgical care at County is
rather decidedly directed toward the treatment of advanced illness instead of oriented in preventive directions. The intern and resident at
County treat many more very sick patients than Cohen physicians do. It
is common to find patients admitted to Cohen Hospital for observation or
for general check-ups. At County, while diagnostic problems are the order of the day, diagnostic attention is chiefly directed toward treatment
of the seriously ill and not toward early detection of possible serious illness. Any morning in the X-ray department at Cohen will find several
patients, in good physical condition, awaiting routine chest and abdominal examinations, as part of the yearly medical exam. The X-ray department at County always finds many patients lying on stretchers, escorted
by attendants, and in rather sickly condition.

Personnel regard the general atmosphere at County as somewhat
depressing. The tenor of activity is relatively morbid; the practice of
medicine and surgery there is predominantly massive in its scope. A good
example is the character of abdominal surgery. At Cohen, there are many
more exploratory laparotomies performed than is the case at County,
where abdominal surgery more often entails radical resection of tissue.
Among its largely lower-class Negro population, there is a rather high rate
of amputations for gangrenous limbs, necessary because of the late detection of disease processes, which are reportedly often the indirect result of
hygienic practices and hard physical work. At Cohen, there is a good deal
of vascular corrective surgery done, e.g., arterial bypasses; at County, the
surgeon encounters a population of much more diseased limbs, requiring
more radical surgical intervention. There is much more facial surgery
done at Cohen, where cancerous or precancerous tissue is removed after
early detection. At County, there is little such surgery performed, for its
patients make their first encounters with the hospital after their conditions are more extremely deteriorated. A large proportion of the operations done at Cohen involve such procedures as cyst excisions, which are
very uncommon at County; at Cohen, there is a good deal of eye surgery
done, e.g., cataract removals and retinal detachments; at County, there is
very little surgery done in this area.

On the medical wards at County, one finds a high frequency of alco-
holism-related diseases, i.e., liver, spleen, and kidney disorders, and many
diabetic patients whose conditions are complicated by alcoholism. There
are many jaundiced patients, so many so that a nurse who came to work
at County after having been employed at a private hospital for many

years, commented, "I've never seen so many yellow people in my whole life." The number of venereal disease patients at County is many times greater than at Cohen. On the surgical floors, one finds a substantial number of patients being treated for traumatic injuries, e.g., gunshot wounds, stab wounds, fractures, concussions, etc.

In this chapter I have tried to present a very general background picture of some prominent aspects of County Hospital. A much more detailed discussion of a variety of organizational features, particularly those relating to death, will be presented in the course of my discussion of specific topics in the following chapters. Rather than ask the reader to keep these features in mind, they shall be introduced at appropriate points in the course of my analysis.

THREE

The Occurrence
and Visibility of Death

Some Ecological and Occupational Considerations

❧❧❧ AT COUNTY HOSPITAL, the occurrence of deaths is relatively frequent. On the average, there are three persons who die in the hospital each day, with variations as great as from none at all to 15 in a given 24-hour period. With 440 beds and an average daily occupancy of 75 per cent, nearly one out of every 110 patients in the hospital, statistically speaking, dies each day. Taking account of the fact that the same patients are frequently readmitted to the hospital within a given year's time, a calculation reveals that nearly 25 per cent of the hospital's patients at any given time will, on the average, die in a bed at County within the course of the year.

Deaths which occur at County Hospital, nearly 1000 per year, are differentially distributed throughout the hospital, with the greatest frequency occurring on the medical and surgical floors, and the least number in the pediatrics, orthopedics, obstetrics, and psychiatric departments. Excluding the approximately 200 beds of the hospital in which deaths very seldom occur, it is found that nearly one out of every 50 patients in the remaining critically ill block of the hospital dies each day. Within this block of beds, constituted by the medical and surgical floors, the statistical likelihood of death is not evenly distributed amongst its 200 beds. As I have noted above, the ward is divided into two sections, that half closest the central corridor being reserved for the more seriously ill patients, the outside half for the ambulatory patients. The critically ill block of the hospital consists of four such wards, designated for "male medicine," "female medicine," "male surgery," and "female surgery." Of the nearly 60 beds on each of these wards, almost all the deaths occur among those patients in the 30 beds of the nonambulatory half of the ward. Roughly 75 per cent of all the deaths in the hospital occur in this critical half of the four medical and surgical wards. In other terms, in approximately one out of every 35 beds in these sections there is a death each day. Making one further specification, warranted by the fact that the proportion of deaths per bed is significantly higher on the medical than on the surgical wards, it can be calculated that about one person in every 25, in these beds of the hospital and again statistically speaking, dies each day.

The personnel on these wards, medicine particularly and surgery as well, therefore encounter death rather frequently. Within the course of his first week on the job, a new orderly or attendant will have assisted in removing several patients' bodies from the ward, the new intern will have pronounced several patients dead, and the new nurses' aide will have wrapped several bodies.

These wards, unlike others in the hospital, are specially oriented to the occurrence of deaths as routine, daily events. This orientation is clearly seen with respect to certain practices related to the processing of a dead body. When a patient dies, his body must be properly prepared before it is removed from the ward. This preparation, which shall be discussed in greater detail in the next chapter, requires, among other things, wrapping the body in a "morgue sheet." The central supply office has such sheets, and assembles them into what is referred to as a "morgue bundle." It includes, in addition to the heavy muslin sheet used to wrap the body, identification tags to be affixed to the corpse, special cotton-covered strings for tying the hands and feet together, and a pair of precut gauze pads which are to be placed over the deceased's eyes. The practice employed by all wards except the medical and surgical ones is to telephone the central supply office when a death occurs and request that a morgue bundle be sent up to the ward. On the medical and surgical wards, however, a large storage of these bundles, usually exceeding several dozen, is kept in the ward supply closet, along with linen and other equipment. As the supply runs low, more are ordered from central supply, much as would be linen, and the fact that there might be few deaths in the course of any given time period would not warrant prolonging an order for new bundles, if the stock was low.

The orientation to death as a continual and routine possibility can be seen also in the fact that on the medical and surgical wards there is always a "morgue tray" kept on hand. When the morgue attendant arrives on most hospital wards to pick up a body for removal to the morgue, he brings a tray with him (the morgue tray, unlike a regular "guerney," is unpadded and has a special top grooved to fit the morgue refrigerator compartments when lifted off its wheels). The medical and surgical wards, however, retain their own morgue stretchers, or trays, which they use if a patient dies after 3:30 P.M. and the morgue attendant is not on duty (the morgue closes for official business at that time). When a death occurs in the late afternoon or evening, ward personnel must remove the body to the morgue themselves. To avoid a long walk to the basement morgue to secure a special tray, or the necessity of having to take the body downstairs on a regular stretcher and then transfer it onto a second fitted tray (a particularly disliked task, especially if one is alone and has to struggle to keep the body from falling off onto the floor), these wards keep such trays on hand. No such equipment is kept permanently on other wards.

Autopsy permits, that legal form which surviving relatives must sign before a postmortem examination may be properly performed, are kept at the nurses' stations throughout the hospital. An interesting difference between medical and surgical and the other service wards relates to the way such forms are assembled: on all but these wards, there is, in a desk drawer at the nurses' station, a series of folders containing the various forms used for varieties of administrative matters, e.g., "consent to perform surgery," "admission," "discharge," "narcotics order," "release of personal belongings," and a host of others. Forms that must be filled out when a death occurs include the "death certificate," the "autopsy permit," the "release of personal belongings" form, and the "provisional death certificate" (a working sheet on which a tentative diagnosis of the "cause of death" is listed before the formal death certificate is completed). On the medical and surgical floors, these "death forms" are stapled together into one unit; it is not uncommon to find the desk clerk, when doing her daily inventories and straightening about during slack hours, collating these forms and assembling them into what is referred to, on these wards, as "death packages." This is not done elsewhere in the hospital, the forms being assembled only if and when a death occurs. While deaths do not occur on the medical and surgical wards with such frequency that the assembling of these forms in advance would seem technically to be required, for instant use as it were, the fact that this is done provides an indication of the way the occurrence of deaths is regarded, namely as events in a class along with all those matters that are the recurrent daily happenings of ward life, and as such are things which an efficient administrative organization considers it proper to prepare for in advance, on at least a day-by-day and not event-to-event basis.

❧ ❧ ❧ COUNTING DEATHS

On high-death wards, staff members frequently ask, upon coming to work, "How many today?" Deaths are counted, not with any special interest, but along with such matters as the number of new admissions, the number of occupied beds, the number of discharges, and other demographic facts. During "report," that ritual wherein the new shift of nurses receives its briefing from the outgoing shift—a changing of the guards—the number of deaths on the previous shift, along with other demographic occurrences, is a matter routinely reported. The opening of the report session, with a staff nurse reviewing nursing care matters with a group of incoming nurses, typically includes the following kinds of prefatory tallies: "We have a full house, Mrs. W was discharged this A.M., a patient is expected in tonight who'll go to Room 7, Mrs. P died this morning"; or "No deaths, three empty beds, quiet night ahead."[1] Then the details of patients' progress and treatment schedules are reviewed. Nurses on these wards leave work at the close of their shift expecting that some of the patients they have cared for during the day will have died during their absence, and frequently they make inquiries upon arriving at work to confirm their expectations. Some nurses characteristically look into doorways of those rooms wherein dying patients had been known to be the day before, to see if they are still alive and present. The following recorded sequents of conversation between nurses at shift change indicate the manner in which such inventories are made and convey a sense of the general import of noticing the occurrence of a death:

> A: Hi Sue, bet you're ready to go home.
>
> B: You ain't just kiddin'—it's been a busy one!
>
> A: What's new?
>
> B: Nothin' much. Oh yes, Mrs. Wilkins, poor soul, died this morning, just after I got here.
>
> A: I didn't think she'd make it that long. Do we have a full house?
>
> B: Just about. Number two's empty, and seven I think.
>
> A: Mrs. Jones die?
>
> B: I think so, let me see. (Looks at charts.) Guess so. (Turns to other nurse.) Did Mrs. Jones die today?
>
> C: She was dead before I got into work this morning, must have died during the night.
>
> A: Poor dear. I hardly knew her but she looked like a nice old lady.

[1] For a discussion of these routine inventories in another hospital setting, see J. Emerson, "Social Functions of Humor in a Hospital," unpublished doctoral dissertation, University of California, Berkeley, 1964, especially Chapter V, "Laughing at Death."

A: You look tired.

B: I am. Lucky you, it's all yours.

A: I hope it's a quiet night. I'm not too enthusiastic.

B: They all died during the day today, lucky us, so you'll probably have it nice and easy.

A: So I saw. Looks like three, four, and five are empty.

B: Can you believe it, we had five deaths in the last twelve hours.

A: How lovely.

B: Well, see you tomorrow night. Have fun.

The announcement of a death from one shift member to another can and does occur in the course of an ordinary greeting conversation, and on these wards, where deaths are not so much announced as they are mentioned, their mention does not noticeably inhibit ordinary conversation. When a death occurs in an unexpected place within the hospital, or when deaths occur in rather unusual circumstances, news spreads quickly and the conversation about death is much more dramatically attenuated. On one occasion, a diabetic woman died in childbirth, a relatively infrequent happening, and by the time a nurse arrived on the OB ward for the evening shift, she had already heard of the morning's death. She was greeted by a daytime nurse as she approached the station with, "Have you heard?" and answered, "Yes, Mrs. B stopped me in the hall downstairs and told me," whereupon a conversation was entered about "what happened" with a level of interest, detailed reporting of "what she said," "why did they do that?" "then what did he do?" etc., far exceeding that which normally attends the discussion of deaths on the medical and surgical wards. On the latter settings, the greeting "have you heard?" would not be taken to refer to a death, unless some rather special circumstance surrounded it, nor would it be used as a way of conveying news of an "ordinary" one.

New student nurses and, apparently, young medical students make it a habit of counting such events as deaths, and locate their own growing experience and sophistication by reference to "how many times" such and such has been encountered, witnessed, done, etc. Throughout the medical world, numerical representations of phenomena are accorded central status as marks of experience. The frequency of encounters with an event, disease type, constellation of symptoms, and the like, is taken to attest significantly to the practitioner's competence and authority and to the warrantability of his suggestions. It is hence useful to consider, if only briefly, some of the ways in which such "counting" occurs and is properly presented.

One apparent mark of sophistication among one's peers is reached at that point when some occurrences are no longer counted, i.e., when "I've lost count" is properly given as an answer. It is instructive to describe the

way this point is achieved. A student nurse informant reported that young
students count, and report their counts in informal conversation, nearly
everything from the number of injections they have given and enemas
administered to the number of operations they have witnessed, autopsies
attended, deaths of their patients, other patients' "dead bodies seen," etc.
Some events, like giving injections and administering enemas, quickly
lose their countability; in fact the count seems to end once the first occasion is superceded by a second. Other events are counted for a more
extensive period of time, and only partially so, it seems, because they accu-
mulate more slowly. While it is apparently relevant to report, "I have
given my first injection today," once that point is reached, the "second
injection" is considered to be of no special interest, e.g., it is not sensibly
used in conversation for demonstrating "more" experience than is attested
by citing the first injection. Experience in giving injections or administering enemas, while perhaps producing skill in doing so, is not conversationally additive as a competence attesting matter, so that having given
one is just as good as having given a hundred.[2] The girl who would report
that she had administered her "second" or "third" injection would be regarded by her peers, my informant reports, as one who was too taken by
the trivial tasks of nursing.

In referring to the fact that specific counts of frequent occurrences
have "long since been lost," we often find persons pointing to that feature
by announcing some number, or using some quasinumerical way of talking which conveys "having lost count" in a somewhat more powerful way.
Examples are "I've given so many injections in my day . . . ," "In the
thousands of operations I have seen . . . ," "I have seen dozens of. . . ."
These kinds of "numerical" ways of describing some state of experience
are to be clearly distinguished from those which involve specific reference
to an actual number, e.g., "I have seen twelve of . . . ," "In the seven
cases of. . . ." Deaths are specifically counted in this latter sense, so it
appears, to about half a dozen. The highest specific (i.e., nonsummary account like "dozens," "hundreds," etc.) count I was able to elicit when asking the question of nurses, "How many have you seen?" was eight. Never
did a student report a figure of more than eight, that number being the
approximate maximum point at which "losing count" occurs, or must be
reported as having occurred. To report a number greater than a handful
is, seemingly, to appear overly concerned about death, in either a worried,
upset, fearful, or over-fascinated way. With respect to deaths, at least, the

---

[2] It is a matter of general sociological interest that a significant transformation occurs
when an event comes to be seen as having ordinal properties, i.e., where it is not
merely an occurrence but one which is seen as an event in a series. A major shift in
ways of looking at the institution of marriage, for example, can be said to attend talk
of a "first marriage."

student can safely say, "I've seen so many I've lost count," and not be sanctioned for pretentiously suggesting "having been around a lot" should the actual number she has witnessed turn out to be just slightly over a handful.

Within any specific setting in the hospital and for different groups in the age-graded and occupational system, there is a culturally defined collection of properly counted items. For the novice, certain grossly de-limited categories of events are counted, e.g., deaths witnessed, operations seen, etc. For nearly everyone but the novice, counts cease to be made in these classes, experience in dealing with them being conveyed by point-ing to the fact that specific counts have "long since been lost."[3] What occurs as one becomes more established in some work setting is that the classes of initially countable events become partitioned into subclasses, the elements of which are themselves counted although those of the class as a whole no longer are. It is relevant and proper—proper in the sense of being sanctionably useable in conversation and not a mark of over-con-cern, naiveté, etc.—to count the "number of children you have seen die," but not the "number of deaths you have witnessed" if that latter number exceeds an handful. Likewise, the student nurse who "rotates" through the operating room counts the number of operations she witnesses up to a few, and then, the student informant reported, it is regarded as strange for her to continue to count and report counts of events in the class "op-erations in general." Further counts would then be made and remembered and reported upon within subcategories, like the number of appendecto-mies, open heart surgeries, gall bladders, and the like.

It can be noted that the differentiation of classes into highly sub-divided classes, and the counting of events within these increasingly dif-ferentiated subclasses, provides a way for demonstrating "experience," "familiarity," and historical involvement in some scene which, unlike the novice's way, via the use of tallies of gross and frequent occurrences, relies on the relative "rareness" of events. Frequently occurring events are counted only for a short time, among newcomers. Old timers seem to maintain numerical tallies of infrequent events, or at least view certain classes of occurrences as prospectively and retrospectively countable, and typically report those tallies by specifying time intervals, e.g., "I haven't

---

[3] It is to be pointed out that the use of this way of talking can be presumptuous for one who, in fact, has not been around very long. "Having lost count," while in any given case perhaps accurately descriptive, is not thereby useable. It is not so much the usage's correctness which warrants it, but what that usage says about its user's claims to certain membership statuses; entitlement to it may be based on other facts: for example, the user's status in the group in which it is used. Among others of his own station an intern will talk of "having lost count" but should an elderly physician be present, an inappropriate disregard for his place as a novitiate in the world of medicine might be conveyed.

seen a woman die in childbirth in five years." The relevant way to report experience with events becomes by reference to their relative as against absolute frequency; the length of expired time between occurrences becomes a sign of experience. By pointing to a relatively rare event (and rare events can be said to be discovered through the process of subdividing general classes into delimited ones) a person proposes his experience by way of the fact that he has been involved in events in which only one who has "been around" would be.

While an extensive discussion of the variant forms, purposes, and conditions of "counting" is beyond the scope of the present discussion, it is relevant to note that as one moves from one scene to another within the hospital, the way deaths are counted shifts. Each scene, as an environment of events, has a culture that prescribes typical frequencies of typical events and domains of infrequent occurrences, the latter of which apparently retain their countable character for long periods of time, even by long-term employees. On the medical and surgical wards all deaths are routinely counted on a daily basis as part of the general demographic inventory which is taken, on a variety of occasions, throughout the work week. While administrative personnel maintain long-term counts of deaths (along with many other events), ward personnel do not add up the daily death counts in any systematic way. In a very busy week a nurse will occasionally and unsolicitedly point to the fact that there have been "lots of deaths" during the week. But no nurse of any tenure on the medical wards can begin to recall the total number of deaths she has witnessed. The day is the relevant unit of temporal specification, and counting "deaths in general" is merely part of counting a host of daily, recurrent happenings. With respect to these wards, one has to ask about some rather special variety of death to elicit specific numerically portrayed descriptions. All the nurses on the medical and surgical wards can with little hesitation report the number of suicidal patients whose deaths they were involved in or which have occurred on their wards during their periods of employment. In conversation with a medical service nurse it can be learned that she remembers that she has seen "two patients die from barium enema exams." (Very infrequently barium enemas produce death when there is a rupture in the intestinal tract and the barium solution escapes into the abdominal cavity; this sort of occurrence, one which can be construed as an error, often becomes a major topic of staff conversation.) Nearly everywhere in the hospital, including the pediatrics ward, personnel can report the number of very young children whose deaths they have witnessed or were in any way involved in. One nurse on that service reported that a particular death was her "thirteenth." If one asks OB nurses, however, to recall how many deaths of newborns they have witnessed, they all (with the exception of the very recent newcomer) report they "have no idea." In certain wards, like the OB ward, adult deaths take on a quite different character. A nurse who was commenting on "delivery room nursing" reported that it was the most "rewarding kind of nursing" with the exception that sometimes it can be very "unpleasant." When questioned about its unpleasantness, she alluded to the fact that when a mother dies in childbirth it can be very upsetting, enough, apparently, to make the ward not altogether a pleasant working place. This nurse was the head of the delivery room nursing division; on further questioning she reported that "seven years ago was the last time one (death) occurred." That single death retained its character as a relevant fact about the OB setting. A senior operating room nurse, of some 30 years' experience on the division, related, on the occasion of a death that occurred on the operating table, that this was the sixth she had seen in her time, that she remembered each vividly, and could describe the circumstances surrounding every one.

The hospital can be viewed as an environment of occurrences, and the place of a death as one hospital occurrence takes on its character as more or less prominent, more or less worth remembering, more or less characteristic of the work of a hospital, etc., depending upon the scenic background of typical occurrences. Particularly noteworthy deaths, those about which lively talk spontaneously occurs, are those which take place in settings where deaths are uncommon, those which occur in atypical fashions, those which result from accidents or diagnostic and treatment errors, and those which result in the very young patient. Any given death, however, is always a potential candidate for later retrospective comment when, for some reason, an instant death suggests a principle of categorization and provides for the relevance of searching over "past ones." So, for example, when a patient died and his wife fainted on the hall corridor when told of his death, a nurse mentioned that that was the third time she had seen a "relative actually faint" at the news of a death. When a patient died during the course of a routine morning round a doctor recounted that he had "had that happen to him," once before in medical school. Any given death is typically discussed by reference to its similarity with others in the past. The more infrequent the occurrence of death on a given ward, the more likely one can elicit talk about death that is specific by virtue of the classification which the ward's specialization naturally provides for, e.g., on the pediatrics ward the discussion of death is immediately directed to the special troubles staff confront in dealing with children's deaths. The more frequent the occurrence of death on a ward, the more talk of death is specially focussed by performing classificatory operations which are not given in the very nature of the ward itself. As hospital events, deaths are attended via their membership in whatever class an instant one lies, and such classification is either given in the fact of a specialized ward, or the result of some classificatory operation designed to delineate the properties of deaths which the character of the ward itself does not immediately suggest. Such concerns as "how horrible death is," "how long he lingered," and such general philosophic considerations do not naturally generate talk and interest in death in daily hospital life, but are only addressed under prodding from an outside party, and then only with difficulty. As organizationally relevant, the commonly discussed aspects of death have to do with ward social structure, i.e., what given death-related occurrences imply about or entail for the activities of ward life and its personnel.

❧❧❧ THE VISIBILITY OF DEATH

Deaths are differentially visible in different parts of the hospital by varying classes of persons according to the ways such persons stand with respect to the occurrence of death occupationally and otherwise, the frequency of deaths in various hospital settings, and certain ecological facts about County. To secretaries in the front business offices, who enter and leave the building via the front door and only superficially enter the hospital proper when they take the elevator to the third floor cafeteria, that "people die at County" is known only via the daily figures they receive from the admission office, upon which they perform numerous accounting operations, e.g., add them up, average them, categorize them, report them in monthly and annual demographic accounts, etc. As a happening of their job setting, "death" consists for them in such figures, about unknown persons, with unknown faces, whose bodies, alive or dead, have never been seen. These personnel are known to purposefully restrict their movements in the building to those places devoid of the life and death aspects of hospital work. The microecology allows and fosters this restriction, for the administrative part of the hospital is nicely separated from the "sick part." Such personnel can work out a career at County, only occasionally ever seeing a patient or smelling those odors associated with the sick parts of the building. The fact that it is a hospital at all consists, for them, merely in that the letters they type, reports they construct, superiors they answer to, and the rest all have something to do with medicine. The only more direct reminder they get of the sick work that goes on at County is in the form of an occasional and faint ambulance siren which is heard in the nearby distance, and in the white coats, gowns, and dresses worn in the cafeteria by nearly everyone but themselves.

Only very infrequently does news of the circumstances surrounding a death ever reach these personnel.[4] One most striking occasion was when

[4] A striking instance of a specially publicized death is given in L. Freeman, *Hospital in Action: The Story of Michael Reese Medical Center* (Skokie, Ill.: Rand McNally & Co., 1956), "The Frozen Woman," pp. 11–21.

a murder occurred at County. A sheriff's deputy, escorting a prisoner to the Emergency Ward, reportedly "went berserk," and shot a secretary for what was regarded as "no reason whatever." The event was the occasion for considerable conversation, gossip, and publicizing. In the Emergency Ward, where personnel routinely treat victims of gunshot wounds, ordinary activity was temporarily disordered. Doctors and nurses stood about peering at the dead woman who lay on the office floor. One nurse was overheard to say to another, "Look at all that blood." For what was to the administrator of the division an embarrassingly long period, no one would approach the body to see if the woman was dead. Generally, the scene resembled a street accident or murder. This kind of "death," not a hospital event at all nor a medically relevant occurrence, but a newsworthy happening, received attention as a full blown incident. While a death, it was not a death-in-an-order, generated as it was not from an illness or accident that occurred outside, but from an internal happening. It was not a "hospital death" but simply a death-in-the-hospital, and as such, did not get treated as do the routine, daily expirations of patients.[5] The usual "death procedures" that produce those statistics which the front office girls handle were absent, so that it was not, for them, or anyone, a work relevant event at all. It is such "deaths" that these personnel might learn of over and above their occupational involvement in death statistics; it is these "deaths in the hospital" about which details of "how it happened," "who discovered the body," "how did he die," and the like, will be discussed. Others in this class that occurred during the period of the investigation included the suicidal death of a psychiatric patient who hanged herself in her room, the heart-attack death of a hospital administrator, and the accidental death of an X-ray technician who electrocuted himself while working with his machinery. As an environment of such events, the hospital falls in a class along with other large organizations, perhaps slightly more susceptible to them by virtue of the frequent presence of police-escorted patients (and in the murder case, the presence of police), the existence of a psychiatric service, and the presence of high-voltage equipment.

The deaths of patients are learned of more directly by medical and nursing staff depending in part upon their particular service location in the hospital and the position of any given nurse or doctor within his respective status hierarchy. The higher one's position as a nurse or doctor in the nursing and medical hierarchies, the less likely one is directly to witness exposed dead bodies, and the still less likely is one apt physically to handle corpses. The nursing administrators and higher echelon physicians will generally encounter dead bodies only as they happen to witness their being transported from the ward to the morgue, after these bodies

[5] Other instances of the deaths of nonpatients is described in the discussion of DOA cases in Chapter 4.

have already been specially wrapped up and covered on a stretcher by a sheet. It is the intern and the ward staff nurse who, among these professional classes, actually view the dead in their beds, though they will not generally handle them, that task being reserved for the nurses' aides and orderlies whose responsibility it is to prepare bodies for transport from the ward. In the next chapter I shall examine the body wrapping task in more detail and discuss the degree of touching of bodies that doctors and nurses do. Here I wish to focus on the general visibility of death within the hospital social structure.

To other patients in the hospital, the occurrence of deaths is more or less known about according to the various methods hospital personnel use for, and controls they exert over, the transport of bodies, conversations about the deaths of patients, and the display of various death-related paraphernalia. The deaths other patients may come to know of, and the bodies they may unwittingly view, are those of persons with whom they may have talked prior to death, heard converse with others, or who stood, vis-à-vis them, as unknown occupants of neighboring beds. On the medical and surgical wards, once a death has been discovered—and that point, as I shall indicate below, is not always coincident with when it occurs—the door to the patient's room is usually closed. On occasion a nurse will post on the door a blank slip of white paper, which is understood by staff as a sign that a dead body lies inside. The door is kept closed until the body has been wrapped and removed from the room by the morgue attendant. While relatives are only infrequently present in the wards at County, when they are in the immediate vicinity of the patient's room there is always the likelihood that they will go into the relative's room and, if not already aware of the death, discover him wrapped up tightly in a bundle. There is also the attended likelihood that a relative by mistake will enter the wrong room, that of a recently deceased, and discover a body. On one occasion, a relative, in a pale white state of apparent shock, half-staggered to the nurses' station to announce what she, correctly, thought she had seen. A doctor was at the station, and he very quickly, detecting what had occurred by the conversation he overheard, offered the account that they had been trying to contact her (the wife) but had not been able to. In an obviously distraught manner he explained that it was standard practice to prepare patients' bodies after death, and that he was extremely sorry she had had to witness her husband in that condition.

The likelihood of such discoveries is very low, primarily because relatives are not often about and because once a body is wrapped up, it is usually transported to the morgue without delay. Additional measures are frequently taken, such as posting a guard outside the door, or fastening it in such a way that it will appear stuck to someone who happens upon it unaware of its occupant. When death occurs in a multibed room, more serious problems of management are presented. Once the death is discovered, the curtains around the bed are drawn as tightly as possible, but that itself is apparently not sufficient to keep the event invisible to others. Several practices are routinely instituted in such cases.

One general preventive policy is to try to assign a patient whose death is expected to a private room. The warrant for such assignment at County, unlike at a middle-class institution like Cohen, seems based almost entirely on the expectation of likely death. At Cohen, and other such institutions, a private room is chosen by the patient and his relatives for various reasons, among which are the concern for privacy, the concern for the patient's welfare, and, it appears in some cases, the mark of status that the cost of such a room implies. At County, the private room is assigned by staff, and while privacy is a value, it is privacy of the expected death that is often at issue, and what that privacy entails in the precautionary measures personnel must take in the treatment of the dying and the death.

As deaths are not always discovered by hospital personnel as soon as they occur, it frequently happens that a roommate will notice the death before members of the staff do. On one occasion, a man yelled hysterically for a nurse, crying aloud, "He's dead," repeatedly, until a staff member arrived. On another occasion a man spent several minutes searching the hall to find a nurse to inform her that the person across from him had just died. Such multibed room deaths are considered especially troublesome affairs from the standpoint of the staff.[6] One of three procedures is generally followed after the death has been discovered. If the other patient or patients are considered "sensitive" to their surroundings, one of two practices generally occurs. Either the deceased patient is placed on a stretcher and removed to another room to be wrapped for discharge to

[6] Numerous examples of patient awareness of death are given in the literature. One study gives the following:

> Three hours elapsed before another nurse came in to discover the death. In the meantime the three living patients had to exist with the horror of one of their number lying dead and uncovered among them.

R. H. Blum *et al.*, *The Management of the Doctor-Patient Relationship* (New York: McGraw-Hill Book Company, 1960), p. 215.

And Orwell, in his "How the Poor Die," writes:

> I could see old Numero 57 lying crumpled up on his side, his face sticking out over the side of the bed, and towards me. He had died some time during the night, nobody knew when. When the nurses came they received news of his death indifferently and went about their work. After a long time, an hour or more, two other nurses marched in abreast like soldiers, with a great clumping of sabots, and knotted up the corpse in the sheets, but it was not removed till some time later.

G. Orwell, "How the Poor Die," in *Shooting an Elephant* (New York: Harcourt, Brace & World, Inc., 1950), p. 25.

the morgue, or, as occurred in several observed instances, the live patient
is taken out of the room under the announced auspices of some purported
procedure. The latter practice only occurs, it seems, when the room is
semiprivate, a two-bed room, and only one live patient has to be removed.
When the dead patient is removed from the room, some care must be
taken to cover the possibility that others might see the patient as he is
removed, and often an attempt is made to make him look alive. On repeated instances, variations on the following example were observed: a
nurse came into the room with an aide, and pretended to be talking to the
patient. "Let's go to X ray," she said, whereupon, with the assistance of
the aide, the patient was transferred from the bed to a stretcher, her head
straightened, mouth closed, and she was quickly and quietly wheeled out
of the room, with the nurse using her body as a screen between the deceased's face and her roommate's bed. Usually, such removal can go unnoticed, at least as can be best discerned from the reactions of other
patients. On occasion, however, a live patient makes some skeptical comment about the dead one, who is being passed off as live, like "Didn't he
just go to X ray?" at which point personnel attempt to give an answer that
will allow them to meet the requirement of getting the body out without
directly confronting the live patient with the fact that it is a body, yet one
that will not be so elaborate as to appear blatantly false. In response to
the question that occurred on one occasion: "Didn't he already go to
X ray?" the aide, who suspected that the live patient had some suspicions
about the liveliness of his roommate, said simply, "Uh huh," and quickly
removed the dead patient. Care must be taken that conversation doesn't
sound too hushed and that, in handling the body, the sounds of that task
are not too loud.

Some personnel are not always sufficiently circumspect in this regard, notable among them being the county coroner, who arrives with a
partner to pick up a coroner's case (e.g., deaths that are the result of accidents, deaths that occur within the first twenty-four hours of a hospital
admittance, so-called "dead on arrival cases," etc.) and rather loudly transfers the body from its bed to the special steel tray used for transport to his
van. On one occasion in the Emergency Unit of the hospital, a man was
seen to hide himself under his bedcovers to make the removal of his dead
roommate less obvious than it was made by the coroner's loud talk and
the clamoring of the steel tray as the body was transferred onto it. He lay
trembling for the duration of the procedure and only with caution and a
nurse's reassurance eventually came out from under the covers.

A common strategy in removing a body from a room where other
patients are potential witnesses of the removal, is to have one staff member engage the live patient(s) in conversation, while others remove the
dead roommate. This frequently occurs when deaths take place in those

parts of the hospital where, by virtue of their low frequency, personnel are not routinely oriented to the possibility of death and do not have institutionalized ways of anticipating deaths, e.g., by assigning "dying" patients to private rooms. The most striking instance of a spontaneous undercover removal of a dead patient was observed on the pediatrics ward, when a young child unexpectedly died in a large ward filled with other children. Nurses on that service, unaccustomed to handling the problems associated with the transport of bodies, were perhaps better able to execute an unnoticed removal, for their concern to do so, unlike that of high death-frequency ward personnel, was not built into some perfunctorily performed and oftentimes sloppy routine. A nurse picked up a ball and threw it to a group of children who were playing at the other end of the room, exclaiming "Let's have a catch." Another nurse assisted in directing their attention away from the dead child's bed, while a doctor and an aide drew the curtains around the bed. A stretcher was brought in and the child quickly transferred to it, while a lively game of catch engrossed the other children's attention, including that of the bedridden who could not participate in the game. A nurse reported that in the hours which followed, none of the children seemed to indicate that they knew what had happened to the boy at the end of the ward, and when one of them asked, the next morning, "Where's that boy?" he seemed satisfied with an answer that he had been transferred to another ward, an answer some variant of which staff members regularly use on the pediatrics ward to explain the absence of a child who has died. Because this death was attended by many personnel, a result in part of the pattern of supervision on the pediatrics ward and the fact that death is considered a more serious matter there, several people were placed in the position of being able to handle quickly problems of the body's visibility.

On the medical and surgical wards, where deaths more often than not occur with no staff members present, the likelihood of discovery by other patients would be greater were it not for the additional facts that most patients on those wards are relatively more ill and are confined to bed and that assignment to private rooms further minimizes the likelihood of discovery by others.[7] To sustain the pattern of infrequent scrutiny that

[7] In such institutions as sanitariums, with largely ambulatory patients, the removal of bodies must be more secretly conducted. Mann provides a fictional account:

> . . . they are very discreetly managed, you understand; you hear nothing of them, or only by chance afterwards; everything is kept strictly private when there is a death, out of regard for other patients, especially the ladies, who might easily get a shock. You don't notice it, even when somebody dies next door. The coffin is brought in very early in the morning, while you are asleep, and the person in question is fetched away at a suitable time too—for instance, while we are eating.

The Magic Mountain (New York: Alfred A. Knopf, Inc., 1958), p. 53.

marks the medical and surgical wards, procedures are instituted to reduce the need for such scrutiny. Those patients expected to "terminate," as hospital language often puts it, are transferred to private parts of the ward; curtains around beds, while not completely concealing, are kept drawn most of the time, so that if a private room is not available, the larger ward is roughly reconstituted into a series of private rooms by the use of the curtains. This arrangement, plus the fact of the generally ill status of most of the patients in those areas of the ward where death is likely to occur, makes the setting of these wards much less conducive to social interaction and the consequent dangers of discovery that a history of friendliness between patients and an interest in the happenings of one's roommates would entail.

As I shall have occasion to note throughout, a great many of the arrangements at County are organized the way they are because of the general confinement of patients to beds and the general absence of relatives or members of the public-at-large in the hospital corridors. It is a quite firm hospital policy for ambulatory patients to be discharged from the hospital as soon as possible after they can again get about, so there are few patients wandering about in the halls. Patients requiring long-term care typically are transferred to the chronic care institution; the use of these interhospital transfers is very frequent. Occasionally, however, on the medical wards a recovering patient—one who is waiting his discharge from the hospital—will be seen walking back and forth on the corridors, chatting with nurses and aides. When such a patient is about, staff members make some slight effort to monitor their conversational references to the deaths of patients, though not always consistently or with success. The morgue attendant, whose job I shall examine in detail below, often arrives at a nursing station to secure a dead patient's chart or the paper bag containing his personal belongings which will accompany his body to the morgue. On several occasions his requests, containing references to the fact of a death's occurrence, were made quite loudly, well within hearing range of the patient or two who happened to be standing near the station. On numerous instances nurses were observed to mention a patient's death when such a bystander was within range. While there would be no purposive reference to such matters in a patient's presence, the degree of care exercised in insuring the privacy of such talk is not always great. Ambulatory patients have been known, on occasion, to converse about the deaths of other patients with members of the staff, particularly lower-echelon personnel like aides, orderlies, and attendants, who seem somewhat less concerned about the privileged character of the knowledge they have. As a characteristic feature of County, the affairs of any given patient are not treated as particularly confidential, nor are their bodies treated with great concern for privacy. In the larger wards curtains are not always drawn about patients' beds during morning rounds so that, particularly on the male medical ward, a patient's body will often be exposed for all in the room to see. The concern for privacy operates somewhat more consistently on the female medical wards, where whenever a woman's breasts or genitals are exposed, curtains are drawn around the bed. Female staff members seem to take greater care to insure that the modesty of patients (and, perhaps, their own) be respected than do male staff members; and among male staff members, the "visiting man," when he makes his morning rounds twice a week, is characteristically that one among the collection of doctors at the bedside who gives the greatest attention to drawing the curtains adequately.

At Cohen Hospital, body exposure is much more seriously protected than at County, and conversation about a patient's condition or a patient's death is usually sealed off from being overheard through the use of a variety of ante-rooms and a more careful control of voice pitch. It seems that the more the institution is open to the public, the more elaborate and enforced are its arrangements for segregating front and backstage activities, and for keeping confidential the relations between particular staff members and members of the family. In the private hospital, like Cohen, doctor-patient-relative interactions are so organized that the privacy of the office setting is roughly maintained ecologically and in spirit when the scene shifts to the hospital. When the private physicians there converse with families they lead them aside, form well-sealed gatherings, and talk in hushed tones, evincing respect both for the relatives' wish to keep family affairs family affairs and their own desire to shield their business from scrutiny by others. The difference can be fairly closely observed, for example, in the ways in which the outcome of a surgical procedure is announced by the physician to family members at County and at Cohen. At County, family members (when there are any and when they are at the hospital) await news of a surgical procedure in that area of the Department of Surgery immediately adjoining the operating rooms. There are several benches in this section, where persons sit while their relatives are in surgery. After the operation, doctors emerge from the operating rooms, and, if they know the family, go to the bench and speak to them. They will discuss the surgery while the relative remains seated at the bench, even if several other people can and do monitor the conversation. Should the relative stand up when being addressed, as often happens, the doctor will not lead him off to a private conversation away from the bench, but will remain close to it. The doctor indicates no special desire to regard the patient's condition as a private matter of discussion; at Cohen, under such circumstances, the physician beckons the family aside and often walks several feet away from others before beginning his account. A more lengthy discussion of the ways in which news is related is found in Chapter 5. It is to be noted that the number of visiting family members per patient is higher at Cohen than at County; throughout County generally, one seldom finds more than one visiting family member per patient, whereas at Cohen there are often as many as a half-dozen relatives and friends. The County physician will typically feel that he has discharged his obligations to account to family members once he converses with the wife, husband, daughter, or son, whomever happens to be at the hospital. At Cohen, the doctor will often be called upon to talk to several members of the family, even if that involves him in moving from one part of the hospital to another, or awaiting the assembly of relatives, some of whom might be in the coffee shop, at another waiting room, etc. On one occasion, typical of many Cohen instances, a doctor who announced the outcome of a surgical procedure to the wife and brother of a patient was then asked to "please come down and talk to Moma," whereupon he went to another area of the floor where the elderly mother was waiting with another family member; the old woman was given an account of the operation, in the course of which the doctor put his arms around the woman, who was noticeably quite nervous, and offered comforting remarks. At County, accountability is not as extensive, nor as intimate, for doctors there will discuss a patient's condition quite formally, with no special efforts made at insulating the conversation from others. Oftentimes at County, the family does not know the physician and the basis for any display of intimacy is apparently absent. In the surgical department, the announcement of the outcome of an operation often involves a public paging of the relative, by a nurse, who has been asked by a physician, "Who are the relatives?" The nurse calls out, "Is a Mrs. X here?" The doctor will use the relative's acknowledgment of her identity to locate her and then proceed to engage her in a relatively public conversation. It is only when a death is announced that more serious effort is made to seal off the conversation from possible onlookers and overhearers. I shall discuss this practice in great detail in Chapter 5. Here, it is to be generally noted that encounters with relatives are, with few exceptions, publicly undertaken. On numerous occasions, in the midst of a busy nursing station and for all to overhear, doctors have been observed to inform relatives that the patient's condition was extremely poor and likely to eventuate in death. As a measure of the degree of concern for privacy during such talk, one can observe a clear difference between the physical distance which separates doctors, or nurses, and family members and patients in daily conversation. The distance separating doctor from family (or, more typically, from *the* relative) at County is often sufficient to allow a person not involved in the encounter to pass between them while walking down the corridor. At Cohen, doctor-patient-relative conversations are so closely conducted, and so removed from the stream of ward traffic, that this would infrequently occur.

The general pattern of nonprivacy and nonconfidentiality that marks both conversations between doctors and relatives and conversations between staff members at County has clear consequences for the general visibility of death and death-related matters. From the standpoint of the investigator, the location of death-related talk and death-related equipment (e.g., morgue trays, death forms, etc.) was much easier at County than at Cohen. The sheer likelihood of hearing the word "autopsy" is greater at County, desipte the fact that the number of autopsies conducted is roughly the same in both settings. On the County medical ward, it is not infrequent to hear such interchanges as the following:

Doctor, from one end of the ward to a doctor at the other end:	"I'm going to the morgue."
Nurse, to an aide, in a large ward room:	"Did they wrap Mrs. S. yet?"
Doctor to doctor, from the nursing station to the middle of the ward corridor:	"Did you pronounce him?"
Nurse, to another, in the presence of a doctor-relative encounter:	"Did they get the autopsy permission?"

The greater absence at County of a nonstaff public operates to instill a general lack of concern for the audience of such remarks. The transport of dead bodies at County is quite different from the procedure used at Cohen. Let me address this matter in some detail, considering some especially interesting aspects of the role of the key specialist in such activities.

❧❧❧ THE MORGUE ATTENDANT

The arrival of the county coroner provides those onlookers who know who he is with clear information about the occurrence of a death. Another person, the morgue attendant of the hospital, is particularly interesting as a similar source of information. As in most hospitals, the County Hospital morgue is located in a relatively inaccessible corner of the hospital basement.[8] To reach it, one must take an elevator to the

---

[8] The stated reason for this universal feature of hospital architecture is that the morgue must be readily accessible to the street to aid in convenient transport of bodies to funeral hearses, and so situated that others will not happen upon it:

> The hospital morgue is best located on the ground floor and placed in an area inaccessible to the general public. It is important that the unit have a suitable exit leading onto a private loading platform which is concealed from hospital patients and the public.

basement from some point in the hospital and walk down the long
underground corridor, past the various shops that comprise the maintenance departments of the hospital. At the far end of this busy corridor,
somewhat hidden around a corner, is the morgue. There is no way to
reach it except by passing the plumbing, carpentry, and electrical shops,
the central supply office, and the hospital laundry. There is one exception, and that is a stairway that leads up from the morgue area to the
Department of Pathology on the first floor. There is no elevator at that
end of the building, so that bodies cannot be transported on stretchers to
the morgue from that locale. This stairway is used by professional personnel, who prefer to enter the morgue without walking the noisy and
busy basement corridor, which is considered to be the province of blue-
collar workers. The morgue attendant, among whose jobs it is to transport bodies from the hospital wards to the morgue, makes, on a typical
day, several trips along this underground corridor, pushing before him
a stretcher, either empty or with a body on top of it. Workers in this part
of the hospital thus frequently witness the transport of "human remains."
The person who accepts a job as an apprentice plumber in the hospital is
likely to find that an object he might have preferred not to see is daily
passed before his eyes. I shall discuss the practice of "body wrapping"
in the next chapter. Here it is important to note that while a dead body is
tightly wrapped in a sheet, and another sheet is employed to drape the
entire stretcher upon which it is transported, it seems reasonably certain
that nearly any onlooker, adult or older child at least, would at a casual
glance see what is on the stretcher. The form of a body, an object between five and six and a half feet long, with bulges at each end and a
rising area in the middle, is quite readily discernible. Objects fitting that
description are not easily conceivable as other than human bodies.[9] On
numerous occasions, the removal of a body was witnessed and from the
gaze of onlookers one could detect that it was a body which was being
seen. Never has an onlooker been observed to regard a sheet-covered
body and not indicate in his glancing manner and subsequent activity
that it was a body he knew he had witnessed. When two or more non-
hospital employees, e.g., relatives, other visitors, patients, and the like,
are with each other and one of them witnesses what he takes to be the

J. K. Owen, *Modern Concepts of Hospital Administration* (Philadelphia: W. B. Saunders Co., 1962), p. 304. Nearly without exception nurses purposefully avoided going
near the morgue, and several persons who worked in that wing of the hospital whose
parking facilities were adjacent to the morgue purposefully parked their cars at
more inconvenient places to avoid having to pass the morgue landing on their way
into the building.
[9] The more so perhaps given the fact that the setting is a hospital and a likely place
to find such objects, although this fact does not appear, in my estimation, to be at all
essential in making the identification.

transport of a body while the other has been looking away, the first very often brings the other's attention to what he is seeing. There is often an interchange between them which gives the impression that the passing object is being pointed out. When one person is alone (particularly a nonstaff person) and sees what he takes to be a body under the sheets of a stretcher, several characteristic forms of reaction can be observed: the person turns away in such a fashion as to indicate that he is not merely shifting his attention but is turning away from something he has seen, e.g., he does so abruptly, with a prior look at the body that indicates he is seeing a body and that makes the turn away seem governed by that perception; women have been observed to cover their eyes, even when alone; one woman was seen to grow rather pale and faint-looking; another was seen to begin a yell or gasp before she covered her mouth.

Staff persons who prefer not to witness the transport of bodies have available to them some systematic ways of avoiding the sight. In the hospital basement, an interesting practice was observed. The morgue attendant, on his way from the hospital morgue to the wards to retrieve a recently deceased patient, provided certain others with information that he was about to be so engaged, allowing them to plan their avoidance of his presence with the body. As he left the morgue to go to a ward, he took that route which he would follow on his return with the body, pushing the stretcher before him. Along the basement corridor at County, each of several maintenance shops is so situated that it constitutes a mere recess in the corridor, and from any point within one of these shops one may monitor the passing of people in the corridor. The morgue attendant explained that several of the men who worked in the maintenance departments, he had learned with experience, characteristically used the fact of his appearance as a way of anticipating that a dead body would soon be pushed past them along the corridor, and that some of them, upon witnessing him pass by with an empty stretcher, made sure that they would have their backs turned to the corridor when he returned with the body. In the plumbing department a man was located who said that whenever he saw "John" go by to get a body he busied himself at his shelf so that when John returned he would probably not be turned towards the corridor. The main door to the laundry room is a Dutch door, the top half of which swings open. A woman is employed in that office whose task it is to receive laundry bundles and give receipts for them. Usually, the top half of the door is kept open. When John passes with his empty stretcher she closes it, anticipating his return. She remarked, "I just don't like to see them" (i.e., bodies).

The morgue attendant's role is sociologically interesting, for his activities are such that he is one of those people in the hospital whose mere presence at a scene indicates a certain event has occurred. When the morgue attendant appears on a ward, personnel who may not know that a death has occurred, or at least do not know that one has not occurred, take his being there as indicating that one has, for his formal responsibilities bring him to a hospital ward only when a death has happened.[10]

For those persons who knew John, his appearance alone, i.e., without the availability of specific information about "why he is here now," served others with a quite restricted range of interpretative possibilities, e.g., upon seeing him, anywhere in the hospital, it would be proper and not a way of joking to ask him, "Who died?"

John was in a rather uncomfortable situation in his movements throughout the hospital, for he was, in a manner of speaking, "trapped by his role." His chief and daily problem was going about the hospital without, wherever he went, appearing to others to be working. Persons engaged in occupations in which they, by virtue of the scope of their activities, appear always "on the job," often make systematic efforts to disclaim the involvements others might possibly see in their presence. John found the hospital too small. Nearly everywhere he went, others could properly view his presence as warranted by the occurrence of a death. He was seen either as going to or having just come from picking up a body or engaging in those gruesome parts of an autopsy in which others knew a morgue attendant to be involved. In an important sense, particularly to the extent that others regarded him as somewhat unclean because of his activities, he was like the proverbial man in a town too small to allow an indiscreet activity to go unnoticed.

John had problems such as how to engage in friendly conversation, how to get someone to sit next to him, or not move away from him, in the hospital cafeteria, how to avoid interrogation by others about "what it is like," and, generally, how to enter any form of ordinary discourse without his affiliation with dead bodies intruding as a prominent way others attended him.

He attempted to convey a sense of not being at work by developing clear styles for use when he wished to provide others a basis for dis-

---

[10] Students of occupations have given attention to the visibility of activities in the appearance of some known person on some scene. The morgue attendant's identity and the known occurrence of an event by way of his appearance are based upon personal acquaintance, or "knowing who he is," coupled with the semipublic definition of his activities as restricted to picking up bodies and doing autopsies. He thus differs, sociologically, from those from whom others obtain information by virtue of a uniform, or by way of particular historical knowledge of some concrete scene in which the appearance of a particular other has special significance. The fact of his being only semipublicly known as the morgue attendant, i.e., only to members of the staff, constituted one of "John's" freedoms: that he could pass before members of the outside public without differing noticeably from other attendants. For a relevant discussion of general strategies of "passing" and the problems of persons having stigmas of various sorts, see E. Goffman, *Stigma* (Englewood Cliffs, N.J.: Prentice-Hall, Inc., 1963), especially Chapter 3.

attending what they inferred his work-relevant attributes to be. His dress furnished one way to set apart nonwork from work activities. Unlike many of the people who wear operating gowns to lunch in the staff cafeteria at County, John made it a habit to change from his gown (the same variety is used in the autopsy procedure as in surgery[11]) to the attendant's uniform before coming to lunch, even if he had an autopsy to assist in directly after lunch. He was the only attendant in the hospital who was ever seen to wear a shirt and tie, which he kept in his locker in the morgue for use on those occasions when he particularly wanted to become detached from his work. He was a good looking, athletically built Negro, who fancied himself as a man with the women in the hospital; on several occasions he was observed to change from his work gown into a shirt and tie in the middle of the day, to take a coffee break with one of the nurses in the lounge where men were permitted. By changing his clothes he attempted to convey a distance from his work activities, both temporally and physically. The blood stains on a surgeon's gown, rather than being signs of messiness, are signs of closeness to a task, and in the case of surgery a considerably prestige-conferring task.[12] The blood stains on a morgue attendant's gown also indicate a closeness to a task, but one which, unlike surgery, brings the operator no particular prestige. Not only did John but other staff members of the Department of Pathology as well changed clothes before coming to lunch.

A general strategy John employed was, upon meeting someone for the first time, to give an ambiguous account of his occupational tasks. Only if necessary and only after friendship was gained when friendship was sought, did he tell others that he worked in the morgue. A preferable account from his standpoint was "I work in the Department of Pathology," or even more detached from that scene, "I am an attendant." When he talked about his work he made a point of highlighting the interesting facts about it and de-emphasizing the grosser aspects, e.g., moving bodies about, mopping the floor of blood after an autopsy, and those other matters which constitute the chief functions he performed.

While he was working, e.g., picking up a body from the ward, he worked quickly, taking no time out for conversation along the way, unless he could manage to leave his stretcher behind and use one of the wards

[11] There are some significant differences in asepsis procedures, however, all of which have to do with the fact that in surgery the protection of the patient from germs is considered important, while in the autopsy it is only the operators' health that is important. So, for example, there is no sterilization of instruments. The masks that are worn are for the operators' protection, not for the "patient's."

[12] Young physicians, particularly interns and first-year residents, characteristically wore blood-stained gowns to the cafeteria, but older physicians did not. One first-year resident was observed in the locker room of the surgical area to change from a clean to dirty, blood-stained gown before going to lunch with a date in the cafeteria.

to which he was going. Whenever he had a stretcher with him, empty or not, he avoided interaction with others, and they with him. One adaptation of his was to carry along a patient's file, or a log book, or some such item, when he was enroute to get a body. Proceeding to the elevator with the body he characteristically engrossed himself in whatever he had brought with him while waiting for the elevator. This made him somewhat less available for visual encounters with others, with the attendant sense of unpleasantness he felt he provided them should they feel obliged out of acquaintanceship or friendship to greet him. As he pushed his occupied stretcher he always looked downward, and on numerous occasions persons with whom he was acquainted and to whom he would have otherwise made an overture of greeting and they the same to him, were silently passed by along his route.

One young nurse's aide whom John reported he was dating was seemingly not put off by the corpses he transported and did not hesitate to engage him in conversation while he was with a body. He appeared uneasy in such conversations with her and tended to laugh nervously about the scene of their engagement while it was in its course, indirectly pointing to what he tried to impress upon her as the impropriety of a friendly conversation while in the presence of a dead person (or to be so seen by others). On one occasion she rested her hand upon the body while talking to him. He got noticeably upset, apparently not so much because he wouldn't do the same (which he did in the confines of the morgue and with persons who stood in occupational relationships to bodies similar to his) but because he felt that as a public behavior (this was in front of the elevator) it was in bad taste, and moreover, it didn't provide for the kind of segregation between himself as a handler of dead bodies and himself as a beau which he considered essential.

In his journey from the hospital ward to the morgue, persons other than staff members would occasionally be passed. At some hospitals, like Cohen, when a death occurs it is a practice to close other patients' doors and try to clear the corridors along which the body must be transported of any nonhospital-employed persons. There is a hard-and-fast rule at Cohen that bodies are not to be removed from rooms during visiting hours. There is a similar rule at County, but neither as hard and fast nor as consistently abided by. At County, no special attempt is made to see if anyone is on the ward before the body is removed from the room and taken down the corridor to the elevator. As for so many activities at County, here too the general absence of relatives and ambulatory patients is taken to make such preparation relatively unnecessary. In a normal afternoon at Cohen, walking from one end of a floor to another would entail passing numerous groups of patients visiting in the halls with their families. At County, throughout the day, such a walk will seldom involve passing such gatherings. Should a nonemployee be on the elevator, an uncomfortably extended containment of corpse and visitor in a small place would occur. The attendant's procedure at the elevator is to stand outside it and wait until it arrives at his floor unoccupied (as I noted above, while these elevators are officially designated for staff members' use, some of the visiting public, what little there is of it, occasionally use them). At Cohen, when a body is to be removed from a ward, an aide, orderly, or nurse goes and gets an elevator, and, only after it has arrived at the floor is the attendant signaled to wheel the body out into the hall and into the elevator. At County, the morgue attendant makes no such preparations, nor do other staff make them for him, so that oftentimes he will stand in front of the publicly visible elevator entrance awaiting the arrival of the car for some time. Should the elevator arrive at his floor and a visitor be in it who is going on to a lower floor, the attendant makes a gesture indicating that he will await the car's return. Should the elevator arrive unoccupied or with a member of the hospital staff in it, he will wheel the body on and stand in front of it, at the front of the elevator, to prohibit any visitor from entering at a lower floor. These elevators, unlike some which hospitals use for such kinds of transportation, do not have devices whose actuation prohibits the elevator from being stopped by persons at floors along the route. John has the feeling that not all staff members should be made to ride downstairs with a body. On occasion, therefore, he lets the elevator go by if a higher-echelon physician or nurse is inside. When inside the elevator, should a doctor or nurse stop the car on a lower floor, en route to the basement, the morgue attendant allows the nurse or doctor to decide whether they wish to ride with a body. He stands in front of the body and only steps aside, letting the nurse or doctor on, if they indicate they don't mind. If he feels they don't know he is concealing a body and proceed to step on the car unknowingly, he calls the fact of his charge to their attention with a remark like "I'm going to the morgue, sir," or "This is a body, sir," as he stands slightly aside to let them see what is behind him. Often doctors and nurses will say, "That's O.K., John," and board the car, but the hospital director and several others have been observed to refrain from riding with the corpse, by saying something like, "Oh, I'll catch it the next time." If a lower-echelon person is awaiting the car at a lower level, John will usually step aside and let him ride down with him, if he wishes to. When people arrive at an elevator entrance and find John standing there with a body, they frequently do not wait for a car, but walk down the stairs, sometimes feeling obliged to announce that they will do that, with a remark like, "Oh, I think I'll walk," often followed by a polite phrase like, "How are things, John?" On numerous occasions nonemployees were watched approaching an elevator to ride down to the main floor and, upon seeing John with a body, turn away to proceed in another direction, giving a sign that they had made some sort of error, had lost their way, or in some other way attempting to avoid open acknowledgement of anxiety about the contact.

Despite his attempts to structure his daily movements so as to segregate his work tasks from his nonwork pursuits—a segregation that was difficult to perform by virtue of his known-about activities and the encompassing character of the hospital setting—John found, as might be expected, that he could not completely dissociate his work from the moral character others imputed to him by virtue of his being so employed. Even in his nonwork hours in the hospital, when he found himself able to engage in ordinary social discourse and could effectively appear as not currently engaged in work, he found himself not especially well-liked. He commented that the thing he found most uncomfortable about the job was not the work entailed by autopsies and body transportation, but the loneliness of that work.

Perhaps in compensation for the character of his job, both its general gruesomeness and the social position it placed him in, he was given both a fairly decent salary, higher than any other attendant or orderly in the hospital, and a fairly wide latitude of authority in the conduct of morgue affairs. The postmortem examination requires the work of two men. One person is needed to do the major work of the examination, and he must be a trained person. Another is necessary to prepare the body for autopsy, assist during the procedure, and clean the autopsy room afterwards. It is interesting to note that the morgue is one of the few areas in the hospital where persons not involved in the medical training program may try their hand at procedures normally performed only by those having certified technical knowledge and skill. Not infrequently the morgue attendant at County began an autopsy procedure himself. This involves making a large incision in the body, from breast-bone to pubic-bone, and opening up layers of fat and muscle until the chest and abdominal cavities are exposed. While the morgue attendant is a relatively skilled person by virtue of having witnessed hundreds of postmortem examinations, he has no special training nor certification in surgical skills. John is known, among pathologists at the hospital, for his expertise in "opening a body," being particularly skilled in doing a cosmetically neat job in removing the brain, a procedure which involves detachment of the skull in such a fashion that after the brain has been removed from the head the skull cap can be replaced with no obvious sign of unnatural fit. This is a man who has no high school education, the lower-class son of a migrant worker. Yet he is quite conversant in the technical details of anatomy and matters pertaining to various pathological conditions. As a "hobby" he reads surgical texts and attends surgical operations. One physician, an assistant resident pathologist, commented (with intended exaggeration but purported respect) that "John knows as much pathology as I do."

In Cohen Hospital, while the chief pathologist is the director of activities in the morgue, a young man, with an undergraduate education and spoken of as something of a "strange fellow," is, in fact, in charge of coordinating many morgue affairs. He is an avid student of disease and anatomy, and keeps an impressive file on the pathological details of all deceased patients, not as part of his job, but for his own "interest."

While the law in some states requires that no parts of the body be permanently removed during autopsy, many parts are in fact not replaced in the abdominal cavity (the usual procedure after organs are examined) before the body is sewn up. Large amounts of tissue are kept for more detailed microscopic analysis, and, occasionally, entire organs are permanently removed. Physicians often register their requests to study certain tissues, so that, for example, some opthamologists leave standing requests to obtain the eyes of all deceased, some urologists, the kidneys, and the pathologist, with permission of surviving relatives, stores these for specialists' research. At County, the morgue attendant went through a period of "study," moving from organ to organ, in which he kept these parts after autopsy and in his spare time dissected them and examined tissue under the microscope. The pathologist legitimated this procedure and recurrently instructed his staff to "be sure and save the————for John."

Should a physician miss an autopsy (physicians are, in principle, expected to attend the postmortem examinations on their own ex-patients whenever possible), the morgue attendant is occasionally asked to fill in details. Interns have been known to use the morgue attendant as a way of getting more detailed information than the laboratory report contained, particularly when they felt that they should be responsible for knowing that detail when "death rounds" were made each weekend, yet when they themselves could not be present at the examination.

The morgue is thus a workable setting, a place where one otherwise untrained can achieve a measure of authority and learn a good deal, as a "hobby," about medicine and surgery.[13] In part, this is because there is little competition for these jobs; pathologists are always pleased to find a worker who will handle many of the details of morgue work which they prefer not to encounter. In return for this help, the attendant is treated, within the morgue context at least, as a semistudent, one to

---

[13] Hospital morgues are reported to serve other functions, as well, among them being as field training centers for student undertakers, as in the case of New York's Bellevue Hospital. See S. R. Cutolo, *Bellevue Is My Home* (Garden City: Doubleday & Company, Inc., 1956), p. 161.

whom it is legitimate to grant access to the use of microscopes, lab equipment, the scalpel, and to whom instruction in a quasi-apprenticeship circumstance can be given. The pathologist at County feels that in treating the attendant as something more than an attendant, he can build interest into an otherwise unpleasant job, retain a good worker, and insure that things get done which might otherwise be avoided or which he might have to do himself.[14] For years at County an older morgue attendant created considerable trouble for the department. He disliked, it was said, cleaning up after autopsies (a particularly messy task) and engaged in systematic subterfuge to avoid having to partake in that procedure. It was said that he would often release bodies to morticians before the autopsy was conducted, by calling them on the phone and telling them that the relatives refused to allow a postmortem. When they came to get the bodies he released them, and, on several occasions, apparently accounted for his behavior to the pathologist by putting blame on the funeral home, proposing that they insisted upon immediate release because the ceremony could not be forestalled any longer. He was reportedly at fault for the development of a series of hostilities between hospital administrators and local mortuary establishments. His behavior was eventually discovered and he was dismissed from the hospital. John, all who knew him maintained, was a "conscientious worker."

---

[14] What in fact seems to happen is that work properly done by trained pathologists becomes defined as "dirty work." The opening of the brain, a rather crude process wherein the scalp is flapped over the face after the skull has been opened with a circular saw, is one of those autopsy procedures which appears sufficiently unpleasant that its conduct can justifiably be given over to the attendant. He is made to feel specially entrusted with a matter of importance, while, in fact, he is relieving physicians of the need to do such butchering themselves.

FOUR

Death and Dying
as Social States of Affairs

❧ ❧ ❧ "DYING" AS A SOCIAL FACT

That a person is "dying" is not an altogether straightforward notion, given the possibility that in a manner of speaking it can properly be said of all persons that, from the moment of birth onward, they move closer to death each day and are, in that sense, continually and forever dying. This recognition is, of course, at the same time both a major resource and dilemma of existential philosophy and literature.

Despite the awareness of continual "dying-from-birth," considered by some as the most profound awareness of man, people in Western society, at least, ordinarily employ "dying" with respect to a rather delimited class of states and persons, and in so doing, seem to confront no great philosophical conflict in saying of that one: "he is dying," yet not admitting the same fact of themselves. It is the more mundane, ordinary use of the characterization the analysis of which is of direct relevance to my concerns. While perhaps philosophically admissible as a description of anyone, the notion "dying" has a strictly circumscribed domain of proper use in the hospital setting. I should like to propose an empirical description of this use, as well as the assessment "he is dead," it too being a somewhat problematic notion.[1]

---

[1] By conceiving of these categories as "problematic" I do not intend at all to suggest that their use is problematic for either professional or lay persons, but rather that, from the sociologist's standpoint, they must be so conceived if the proper analytic attitude toward them is to be maintained. I intend the term "problematic"

It is to be noted from the outset that the characterizations "he is dead" and "he is dying" (as well as their chief lexical variants in the hospital setting: "he is deceased" and "he is terminally ill"), are the products of assessment procedures, i.e., constitute the outcomes of investigative inquiries of more or less detail, undertaken by persons more or less practically involved in the consequences that discovery of those outcomes foreseeably have. To be "dead" or "dying" is, from our sociological perspective, to be so regarded by those who routinely and rightfully engage in assessing those states and premising courses of action, both for themselves and others, on the basis of these assessments. An interest we take in these phenomena is directed towards explicating how these assessments are made and reported upon within the organizational milieu of the hospital social system. I shall begin by considering "dying" and then move to treat "death." This chapter shall focus on these facts as organizationally relevant matters; the next shall devote attention to the activities of reporting on them.

It is perhaps not altogether impossible to conceive of the circumstance where "dying" was not a matter which persons attended to, where persons simply died, for varieties of reasons, and where, at the time of the death it would be regarded as strange to be asked to retrospectively locate that point at which "dying" could be said to have begun, e.g., "he started last year." The philosophic recognition that "dying" begins when life does might seem to make such a location attempt quite arbitrary, if not meaningless.

Yet deaths occur in a social order. The thoughts, concerns, activities, projects, prospects, and fate of others are more or less linked to the one who dies and the fact of his death. The character of this linkage is partially given by the location of the person in a variety of social structures, e.g., the family, the hospital, the occupationally structured careers of the society, the age-graded system generally, etc., and it provides, in turn, for the varying degrees of relevance of anticipating death and programming courses of action on the basis of such an anticipation. Death occurs in an organizationally based medical order as well. The programming of courses of treatment, the activities of diagnosis and prognosis, the appropriation of time, interest, and money—these are among the practical and sanctionable concerns of the medical professionals, and the anticipation of persons' deaths figures prominently into the way such concerns are concretely organized.[2]

---

in accord with Harold Garfinkel's usage, as for example in his "Studies in the Routine Grounds of Everyday Activities," *Social Problems*, 11, No. 3 (Winter, 1964), 235–250.

[2] Of relevance to this analysis is Glaser and Strauss and their "Awareness Contexts and

"Dying" comes to be noticed at certain points and not others in the course of a life, despite the existential proposition of dying-from-birth, and whatever the medical basis of its proper recognition (and that perhaps is problematic), there are many respects in which the most criterial features of the notion's use have to do with explicitly social considerations. It is these I propose to explore.

The medical, or biological, or physiochemical basis for regarding a person as "dying" are not entirely clear. Noticing "dying" seems to be a quite different order of conceptual activity from noticing bleeding, or fibrillating, or employing a disease category to organize some set of symptoms and findings. As a "medical category," "dying" seems clearly distinguished from disease categories on one hand and bio-chemico-physical states and processes on the other. "Dying" does not, in the American system of medicine at least, stand as an appropriate answer to questions on the order of "what's wrong with me, doctor?"—which questions seem partially definitive of "diseases." Disease categories can be said to consist of those linguistic items that can properly be taken to stand as answers to ques-

---

Social Interaction," *American Sociological Review*, 29 (October, 1964), 669–678. See also their book, *Awareness of Dying* (Chicago: Aldine Publishing Co., 1965). A key difference between my approach and theirs is that in their analysis, what "dying" consists of is not treated as a problematic phenomenon. Their central interest, of considerable social-psychological importance, is the management of information in interaction; their central issue is "awareness of dying" and for their purposes what "dying" is has not been accorded central attention. I have found it necessary, being less concerned with interaction between staff and patient and more concerned with the organization of ward activities, to regard the very phenomenon of "dying" as troublesome, an understanding of its sense requiring location of those practices which its use warrants.

Generally, I have not considered the "patient's knowledge" of the likelihood of his own forthcoming death, a topic of considerable interest and one which Glaser and Strauss treat in detail. Only infrequently in my observations at County did I encounter conversations between staff and patients about forthcoming death, or among staff about patients' awarenesses. The deaths I witnessed seldom involved a patient whose condition was such that interaction with him was likely. It is my feeling that a considerable number of deaths involve the circumstance where awareness of "dying" is irrelevant, from an organizational perspective, with a chief exception being cancer, where both patients and staff members are involved in daily social interaction. Deaths of patients suffering from other diseases, e.g., heart disease, kidney disease, CVA's (strokes), and liver diseases, have a course such that at that point when "dying" becomes noticeable, during the patient's "last admission" to the hospital, the patient is, so to speak, out of the picture. The greatest "cause of death," heart disease, typically "produces" death in the course of a short-term hospital admission, eventuating from an "attack" and is not preceded by that lengthy period of consciousness which is the fate of the cancer victim.

For other discussions of "awareness" see S. Standard and H. Nathan, *Should the Patient Know the Truth?* (New York: Springer Publishing Co., Inc., 1955); W. D. Kelly and S. R. Friesen, "Do Cancer Patients Want to Be Told?" *Surgery*, 27 (1950), 822; M. Field, *Patients Are People* (New York: Columbia University Press, 1953), pp. 72–76.

tions taking the form "what's wrong with me?" or "what have I got?"
"Dying" does not properly stand as such an answer.[3]

The question "what's wrong with me (or him, etc.)?" does not always
elicit a disease category as an answer but does, on occasion, elicit an
enumeration of some set of symptoms or purported happenings or conditions. So the question "what's wrong with him?" may elicit, as proper
responses, "he has X," "he complains of X," "he is X-ing," and, of course,
variations on "I don't know." The elements of enumerations, when they
are given, may or may not be organizable into some disease category or
categories. "Dying" however, is not an appropriate descriptive term in
such enumerations as they occur in our society generally and in the
medical world specifically.

"Dying" seems to be an essentially predictive term. It appears to
be the case that when nurses in the hospital say "you can tell that someone is dying just by looking at them," what they are pointing to is the
fact that given some set of observable happenings, or known about happenings, or assumed happenings, death is likely to occur in such and such
a period of time. Seeing "dying" is seeing the likelihood of death within
some temporal perspective; it is not like seeing a cancer, or seeing shock,
or seeing bleeding. In the medical world one learns to see dying when, in
the course of his experience with critically ill persons, he can learn to
detect signs which warrant a particular order of time-specific death predictions.

What the existential proposition of "dying-from-birth" may perhaps provide is an extended temporal perspective based on the recognition of man's mortality; the actuarial table provides a more specified
age-graded system of temporal reference brackets in terms of which
"death" can be statistically predicted; disease categories, symptoms, and
biochemical happenings—the data and conceptual apparatus of medicine—provide a still more specified temporal perspective. So the exis-
tentialist can, in his philosophical moments, regard the newborn baby
(or yet-to-be-born fetus) as "dying"; and the insurance salesman, in his
calculation of premium rates (the likelihood of "deaths" within varying
specifiable times), predict death with varying degrees of accuracy; and the
physician or nurse, or person otherwise knowledgeable in matters of
illness, the likelihood of "death" given X and Y symptoms, or happenings, or diseases.

What the medical perspective on life provides, via the use of
diseases and biological events generally as prognosticators, is another
among a variety of possible timetables in terms of which predictions of

[3] This conception of "disease categories" is taken from the excellent paper by Charles
Frake, "The Diagnosis of Disease Among the Subanun of Mindanao," *American
Anthropologist*, 63 (1961), 113–132.

"death" or talk of "dying" are framed. In our society, at least, medical people seem to have obtained a franchise on the notion of "dying," despite the philosopher's existential recognition and the insurance man's predictive tables. If one seeks to know if he is "dying" he consults his physician, not his insurance broker. There appears to be some special power to the notion of "fatal illness," such that the philosopher's description of "life as a fatal illness" does not constitute a threat but the doctor's discovery of a cancer does. Wherein that special power lies is a matter of some interest; first, the notion of the "fatal illness" requires comment.

To say of a person that he "died from cancer" is, in some circles, e.g., that of medical pathologists, a somewhat strange way of talking.[4] The actual occurrence of a death involves the operation of a rather specific set of mechanisms, none of which is currently understood in great detail, and none of which is specifically included under the general rubric *cancer*, neither as its definitive features, nor as cancer's specific inevitable consequences. To "die," some say, the heart must cease beating, and that can occur as a direct result of one or more of a series of quite specific bio-chemico-physical occurrences, e.g., the heart can burst open in certain kinds of trauma, the nerve tissue which provides the heart with its electrical stimulation can be damaged, or weakened through a loss of blood supply, etc. Yet cessation of the heart is currently considered by some to be merely a "sign" of death, and not definitive of it. In certain medical circles there is considerable disagreement over the precise biological meaning of death; some argue that the cessation of cellular activity constitutes death, others insist upon a more specific attention to properties of cellular multiplication; all generally agree that the definition of "death" that will be most satisfactory will be one based on an understanding of life's specific mechanisms and not "disease categories," which can be regarded as only "predisposing conditions." As predisposing conditions they constitute, or some of them— the so-called "fatal illnesses"—constitute good predictors of death, i.e., their located presence warrants making a prediction of death within limits that could not be specified without their location.

Some persons argue that "dying" is a thing which becomes recognizable once such a deadly disease is located, i.e., that "dying" is a state wherein a person suffers from a disease which is nonreversible and is known to "produce death." For purposes of setting up my argument, let me examine this position from a somewhat critical perspective. An argu-

[4] See R. Pearl, *The Biology of Death* (Philadelphia: J. B. Lippincott Co., 1922), particularly pp. 102–110, and W. Riese, *The Conception of Disease* (New York: Philosophical Library, Inc., 1953). When pathologists give reports on the cause of death in the course of hospital "death rounds" their descriptions generally make no mention of a "disease," but rather, a detailed tracing of lesions and a sequential account of the progressive destruction of cellular tissue are provided.

ment with lay conceptions is not intended. My concern in regarding
them critically is eventually to focus on their definitive features.

On one count, location of a "death-causing disease" does not warrant
talk of "dying," namely that talk occurs when a disease of this character cannot be located, i.e., when certain symptoms, biological events,
or conditions are noticed but where the organization of those matters into a disease category cannot, for a variety of reasons, be successfully achieved. The patient who arrives in the Emergency Ward of
County in a state of deep "shock" may be considered "dying," even
though no disease has been cited as a description or causal account of his
condition. The disease may be discovered retrospectively, at an autopsy,
or there may be no disease whatever, the death being described as
due to some traumatic occurrence, e.g., the ingestion of a barbituate, a
gunshot wound, etc.

On another count, the location of a "death-causing disease" does
not warrant talk of "dying"—namely, that the present set of diseases does
not, in any strict sense, stand as an adequate causal account of death.
On still a third count, the location of a "death-causing disease" does not
exclusively warrant talk and treatment of a person as "dying," for persons with such "diseases" are not always so regarded. In the hospital,
an 85-year-old man with advanced arteriosclerosis will not always, on
the basis of the disease itself, be regarded as a "dying man."

In nearly every hospital in the U.S. there is a book one will find at
nurses' stations, on doctors' desks, and in the hospital morgue, that
contains a lengthy list of items headed "causes of death," any one of which
can properly be entered in the legal death certificate where the "cause
of death" is asked for.[5] In addition to disease categories, like "carcinoma
of the stomach," "myocardial infarction," and the rest, are certain
physical occurrences that are considered "nonnatural," like "poisoning,"
"drowning," "natural amputation," etc. These "causes of death" consist of
those diseases, physical occurrences, and the like that are legally taken
as sufficient explanations of the death, i.e., they stand as legitimate, adequate answers to the question: "Why did he die?"; they are answers for
recording on the death certificate, for telling members of the deceased's
family why he died, for satisfying insurance requirements for a "natural
death," etc. Their adequacy as accounts is a legal and socially given adequacy and not a biochemically descriptive adequacy.

The collection of diseases, including the so-called "fatal illnesses,"
which medicine, at any point in its development, employs in organizing
treatment, teaching its students, filling out death certificates, and the like,
is a product of the current state of medical knowledge. As that knowledge

[5] American Medical Association, *Standard Nomenclature of Diseases and Operations,*
4th edition, (Philadelphia: Blakiston, 1952).

changes, the culturally defined collection of disease categories becomes more elaborate; diseases that were previously considered independent of one another come to be recognized, under the auspices of new principles of organizing biochemical facts, as related in formerly unrecognized ways; diseases that were earlier thought to be varieties of some more generic diseases come to be regarded as worthy of independent status as distinctive entities; new diseases are discovered; etc.[6] That *cancer*, for example, is now regarded as a "fatal illness" and a prevalent "cause of death" is a function of the direction which medical inquiry currently takes. It is conceivable (and indeed a goal of researchers in this field) that as cancer's mechanisms are better understood, the antecedents of cancer will become more precisely locatable, so that one may detect this "fatal illness" in its presymptomatic stages, perhaps to the extent that a new order of phenomenon, having to do with the multiplying propensities of certain cellular structures, becomes designated as the "fatal illness." In some important senses, it can be said that the goal of medical research is to locate the fatal illnesses we all contain within us—a principled medical description of "life as a fatal illness."

The point of the above paragraphs is to suggest that currently available and employed categories of diseases, as sanctionably used "causes of death" are culturally constituted entities, and that death is an "outcome" of "diseases" in a socially sanctioned manner of speaking, but not in any strict biochemical sense.[7] What seems to set off the cancer patients from the "well," or at least some cancer patients, is not simply that they have a "fatal disease which will kill them," for it can be said of all of us that we have "fatal diseases in progress" which will kill us and which could be located (and perhaps will be) were it not for the particular diagnostic direction medical inquiry currently takes and the current

---

[6] For discussions of the changing character of disease categories see R. Dubos, *Mirage of Health* (Garden City, N.Y.: Doubleday & Company, Inc., 1961), especially Chapters IV and VI; H. E. Sigarest, *A History of Medicine*, 2 volumes (New York: Oxford University Press, Inc., 1951); and Sir James Spence, "The Methodology of the Clinical Sciences," in *Lectures on the Scientific Basis of Medicine* (London: Athlono Press, 1952–53), Volume II, pp. 1–14.

A listing of "causes of death" in 1736 in London included "apoplexy," "old age," "lunacy," and "jaundice." "Old age" was the largest "killer." See *The Gentleman's Magazine and the London Bill of Mortality, 1731–1778* (New Jersey: Ross Paxton, 1963), p. 24.

[7] The juxtaposition of "biochemical" and "social" is here intended merely for the sake of my argument, which is, in fact, that such distinctions are not necessarily viable. As in the case with the concepts "death" and "dying" so it is expectably the case with other hard-and-fast natural dichotomies, namely, that they are through and through socially constituted. The very biologic determination of death as a judgmental activity performed by actors in an organizational environment, can be seen as itself a socially prescribed activity. For a brilliant analysis of sexual status which treats the issue of "natural" facts of life in detail, see H. Garfinkel, "Passing and the Management of Achieved Sexual Status in an Intersexed Person," U.C.L.A., mimeographed.

state of medical knowledge. A partially distinguishing fact about the cancer patient is the degree of accuracy with which predictions of his death within some specifiable time period can be made by virtue of the detected presence of a cancerous growth; and that predictive accuracy is the outcome, in turn, of the fact that medical people spend a great deal of time developing prognostic indicators and fatality tables for the disease *cancer*. It is to be noted, of course, that actuarial tables provide a reasonably accurate basis for temporally specifying predictions of death. So that, for example, the 80-year-old with no locatable disease of a so-called "fatal" character, can statistically be predicted to die within a short time period and with as much predictive accuracy as the person with a newly developed cancer.

Yet such an 80-year-old will not, in our society, always be conceived as "dying," nor in the hospital as a "terminal patient." If predictive accuracy in foreseeing death within specifiable time periods and the location of a so-called "fatal illness" are not, in themselves, sufficient conditions for conceiving of a person as "dying"—and given the way that notion is used they appear not to be—then what is? The 80-year-old who develops carcinoma of the stomach will not always be regarded as "dying," yet the 20-year-old who develops Hodgkins Disease often will be.

It can be suggested that the answer seems to lie in the way temporal specification of a prediction of forthcoming death is linked *1.* to the person's location along the temporal dimensions of a variety of social structures and *2.* the way temporal specifications of predictions of death involve those who make them in a variety of organizational, interactional, and professional problems. I shall consider each of these forms of linkage in turn and argue that an understanding of them is required to grasp adequately what the notion of "dying" means within the hospital context.

That a 20-year-old is expected to die in 10 years is, in our society, an apparently more relevant fact than that a 75-year-old may have a similar length of time to live before his death, and that relevance has to do, it seems, with the respective place of each in a variety of social structures. "Dying" becomes an important, noticeable "process" insofar as it serves to provide others, as well as the patient, with a way to orient to the future, to organize activities around the expectability of death, to "prepare for it." The notion of "dying" appears to be a distinctly social one, for its central relevance is provided for by the fact that it establishes a way of attending a person. Physicians and nurses don't treat "dying" but diseases and symptoms and happenings, yet they seem to have a special way of regarding and caring for persons once they come to conceive of them as "dying." In the hospital, as elsewhere, what the notion of "dying" does, as a predictive characterization, is place a frame of interpretation around a person. What that frame entails in the way of concrete social activities shall be the topic of the remaining sections of this chapter.

In the County hospital setting, the greatest proportion of patients, over 75 per cent, are over 60 years of age. The mere location of a "fatal illness" does not, for hospital personnel, warrant employing "dying," or "terminality," with any special sense. Many of County's patients have locatable "fatal illnesses," i.e., illnesses which, should the person die, could appropriately be entered on a death certificate as "causes of death." The patient population includes many persons with advanced carcinomas, arteriosclerotic heart disease, severe liver and kidney malfunctioning, etc.

Generally and ideally, for persons so located in the age structure of the society, the fact of their eventual and perhaps shortly upcoming deaths is attended by family members; the social structures in which they are involved are oriented to the fact of their forthcoming death; their families have become increasingly independent of them; the scope of references to the "future" has progressively narrowed; their careers are regarded retrospectively and not prospectively.[8] It is considered proper to treat the "fact" of their "dying" as of considerably less consequence for others, e.g., it is not felt to be a matter requiring drastic revision of others' life plans, as does the "fact" that a young adult is "dying."

Physicians, in treating and attending their elderly patients, do not regard the fact of "death within ten years" as warranting any special consideration (though that fact is a very basic one as regards the way the whole structure of medical practice with the elderly is organized). In dealing with elderly patients, there need be no conscious avoidance of future references, as is characteristically the case in conversing with the young adult who is expected to die within an abnormally short time period. Such references are, in our society, systematically and "naturally" dropped from conversation with the aged. A most noticeable fact about interaction between medical personnel and young "dying" patients is the careful avoidance of long-term future references. A nurse reported about her trouble in talking to a young teenager who was "dying" of Hodgkins Disease and knew her life span was expectably short: the greatest problem she experienced was to keep from talking about plans for school, a marriage, a career, etc. In conversing with the elderly, in our society, the

---

[8] For a general discussion of the disengagement of the elderly from ongoing social life, see E. Cummings and W. Henry, *Growing Old* (New York: Basic Books, 1961), especially Chapter XII. For an extended treatment of the place of the elderly in non-Western societies, see L. Simmons, *The Role of the Aged in Primitive Societies* (New Haven: Yale University Press, 1945).

future becomes attended as the days and the weeks to follow and "dying," the older the patient, comes to mean for hospital personnel *dying on this admission to the hospital*. That the patient may die within the year or the month becomes, within the hospital context at least, a manageable possibility so long as the patient is old, i.e., a possibility that requires no special daily interactional contortions, no planned avoidance of death and the future as conversational topics.

With the young person, noticing "dying" is a crucial matter as regards certain interactional problems. A young teenager at County had moderately advanced leukemia, a disease that often does not seriously debilitate its victim until its very late stages. This girl was in the ambulatory section of the female medical ward and spent most of her days in the hospital walking up and down the corridors (she came to County during the critical phases of her illness; in the course of several years she was purportedly in and out of the hospital dozens of times, a characteristic hospital career pattern for patients with this disease). A new member of the nursing staff engaged her in conversation on the first day of a new admission, and, in the course of talking about those things which one talks with teenage girls about, e.g., "do you have a boyfriend," "when do you want to get married?" etc., the girl, who was said to be "very mature" in her attitude toward her illness, interrupted the nurse with the announcement: "I'm going to die in a few years and have learned not to think about such things." The nurse was visibly upset by the fact that she had unwittingly led the conversation in such directions; other nurses apologized for not having told her about the facts of the case.

Few such cases are available from my data at County, where the average age of the patient population is well over 50.[9] In the local area there are several specialized children's hospitals and teaching hospitals which accept "charity cases," so that County treats very few young "dying" patients. Of the some 250 deaths on which my observations are based only a handful involved persons under 40 years old.

With the average County patients, the danger of unwittingly entering conversation inappropriate with a "dying" patient is relatively nonexistent, for on one hand few of the hospital's patients are in any condition for sociable interaction, and conversation with the "dying"—in County the elderly—need not be specially modified insofar as the things

---

[9] Glaser and Strauss, "Awareness Contexts and Social Interaction," *op. cit.*, pp. 55–56, locate the control of future references in the degree of awareness staff have of the patients' conditions. While that is certainly an important determinant, as is seen in the example cited above, my argument is that a considerable amount of "natural control" is provided for by the general way in which older persons are treated within limited temporal perspectives. "Awareness" is most relevant only with patients with whom, were staff not aware, matters like the future would relevantly be discussed, i.e., the nonelderly.

one normally discusses with them are not premised on, or take their meaning from, any understanding of a long-term future. At County, "dying" shifts in importance from a fact the notice of which is of great relevance as a basis for attending the younger person within a long-term temporal perspective, e.g., in terms of a career, family, etc., to a fact the relevance of which, with the elderly, is great only if death is considered an imminent possibility. For hospital personnel, the domain of relevant considerations is the hospital organization and the activities that go on within it, and "dying" takes its central sense against the background of these activities. The older the patient, the more readily hospital personnel can attend the expectation of death within years, and restrict the sense of "dying" to "dying this time."

There are, of course, exceptions to the general tendency for "dying" to become increasingly restricted in temporal reference and significance with age; the most notable instances are those where the person whose death is contemplated occupies some special place in the wider social structure. That an elder statesman is expected to die within the term of his office, can become a quite relevant matter; and "dying" in the case of an elderly man can be of utmost import to, for example, an heir-to-be awaiting his inheritance, or those members of the family whose daily activities may be severely restricted by the care they give their aging relative. Where the social consequences of death are taken to be of greater import we find reference to the fact of "dying" made within more extended temporal schema of anticipation.

In the hospital setting, however, "dying" takes on its central significance insofar as death is considered likely on the current admission, for it is then that the hospital, its personnel, and its activities are directly involved in the affair of the death. That all very old patients are, in some more general sense of the term, "dying" is an irrelevant issue, not because of the absence or presence of "fatal diseases" but because the consequences of regarding them in that way are both immaterial from the standpoint of the hospital's activities, and, it could be argued, quite detrimental to the ideological organization of medical practice with the elderly. For physicians to assume an existential posture toward death, or operate under the auspices of an actuarial calculus, would seem to undercut the central notion that the doctor's job is to "prevent death." That the greatest proportion of very ill patients in our society are elderly, provides for the essential importance of restricting the temporal confines of predictions of death and action based upon an assessment of inevitable demise. In orienting his daily treatment activities with the elderly, the physician must develop the ability to disattend the possibility of death, unless it is quite imminent. Pessimism about life and actions based on that pessimism seem warranted, in the medical world at least, only when death becomes contemplated within the temporal confines of the hospital-doctor-patient-relative contractual relationship, and that temporally bounded contract, at County Hospital, extends little beyond the boundaries of any given hospital admission. The case of the private physician, with a different kind of contractual involvement in the affairs of his patient, within a more extended temporal matrix, is presumably quite different. Dying takes on a more extended temporal significance to the degree that the physician is more implicated into the social worlds of his patients and their families, and when his patients are recurrently his patients.

The "dying" patients at County are those who are expected to die within the course of their present hospital admission. As a short term, acute treatment institution, this course seldom exceeds 10 or 15 days. Let me now turn to examine some of the activities that recognition of "dying" seems to entail in the treatment of patients during the expected final week of life. Later, I shall consider some of the ways in which that recognition of likely death is achieved, pointing to certain central structural constraints that set the conditions under which the recognition is properly employed as a basis for treatment. Following that discussion, I shall turn to consider "death" as a decisional matter.

❧❧❧ "SOCIAL DEATH"[10]

When, in the course of a patient's illness his condition is considered such that he is "dying" or "terminally ill," his name is "posted" on the "critical patients' list." Once "posted" a patient has the theoretical right to receive visitors throughout the day and night and not merely at the appointed visiting hours. Posting also serves as an internally relevant message, notifying certain key hospital personnel that a death may be forthcoming and that appropriate preparations for that possibility are tentatively warranted. In the hospital morgue, scheduling is an important requirement. Rough first drafts of the week's expected work load are made, with the number of possible autopsies being a matter which, if possible, is to be anticipated and planned for. In making such estimates the morgue attendant consults "posted lists" from which he makes a guess as to the work load of the coming week. The "posted list" is also consulted by various medical personnel who have some special interest in various anatomical regions. County's morgue attendant made it a practice to alert the ward physician that Doctor S. wanted to get all the eyes he could (Doctor S. was a research ophthalmologist). To provide Dr.

---

[10] During the course of observations in a mental institution, Erving Goffman observed predeath treatments of patients. It was he who first directed my attention to the notion of "social death." My restricted usage of the notion does not necessarily coincide with his intended interest in it.

S. with the needed eyes, the morgue attendant habitually checked the "posted list" and tried, in informal talk with the nurses about the patient's family, to assess his chances of getting the family's permission to relinquish the eyes of the patient for research. Apparently, when he felt he had located a likely candidate, a patient whose family could be expected to give permission at the time of death, he thus informed the pathologist, who made an effort, via the resident physician, to have special attention given to the request for an eye donation. (At several places in the hospital: on the admission nurse's desk, in the morgue, in doctors' lounges, and elsewhere, there were periodically placed signs that read "Dr. S. needs eyes," "Dr. Y. needs kidneys," etc.)

At County there is a Catholic chaplain whose main responsibility, it seems, is administering last rites. Each morning he makes "rounds" through the various wards of the hospital. At each ward, he consults a master schedule, which is an index file containing patients' names, religions, sex, and diagnoses. All patients who have been posted are identified with a red plastic border which is placed on their cards. The chaplain goes through this file daily and writes down the names of all known Catholic patients who have been posted, whereupon he enters these patients' rooms and administers extreme unction. After completing his round on each ward, he stamps the index card of the patient with a rubber stamp which reads:

Last Rites Administered

Date_____ Clergyman_____

Each day he consults the files anew to see if new patients have been admitted to the wards and/or put on the critical list. His stamp serves to prevent him from performing the rites twice on the same patient.

In fact, many "posted patients" do not die, for "posting" is often done well before obvious impending death is noted. Quite a few people therefore leave County alive, yet formally relieved of their earthly sins. The priest reported that such cleansing is not permanent, however, and that upon readmission to the hospital one must, before he dies, receive last rites again; the first administration is no longer operative.

It is significant that some seriously ill "posted patients" can be properly regarded as prospective candidates for autopsies before their deaths, a conception not entertained at Cohen Hospital. Indicative of the general stance taken toward some dying patients at County is the following conversation that occurred between two resident physicians at the bedside of a "terminally ill patient" in the first stages of a coma from uremic poisoning:

A: Do you think, really, that both kidneys are as bad?
B: I know they're both bad because the output is so damned low. Let's put it this way, neither one is good.

A: Well, we'll find out for sure at autopsy.

B: Right.

To discuss a patient's forthcoming autopsy, while that patient is still a patient, would be severely sanctioned at Cohen, without respect for the fact that the patient might be considered "comatose" and not aware of conversation in his presence. At County, there is a decided phasing-out of attention given to "dying" patients, such that the possibility of death within the period of a given work shift itself is taken to warrant instituting certain forms of postdeath treatment.

A tentative distinction can be made between "clinical death": the appearance of "death signs" upon physical examination; "biological death": the cessation of cellular activity; and a third category, "social death" which, within the hospital setting, is marked by that point at which a patient is treated essentially as a corpse, though perhaps still "clinically" and "biologically" alive. The following example is illustrative of what is intended by the term "social death": A nurse on duty with a woman who she explained was "dying," was observed to spend some two or three minutes trying to close the woman's eyelids. This involved slowly but somewhat forcefully pushing the two lids together to get them to adhere in a closed position. After several unsuccessful moments she managed to get them to stay shut and said, with a sigh of accomplishment, "Now they're right." When questioned about what she had been doing, she reported that a patient's eyelids are always closed after death, so that the body will resemble a sleeping person. After death, however, she reported, it was more difficult to accomplish a complete lid closure, especially after the body muscles have begun to tighten; the eyelids become less pliable, more resistant, and have a tendency to move apart; she always tried, she reported, to close them before death; while the eyes are still elastic they are more easily manipulated. This allowed ward personnel to more quickly wrap the body upon death (if death indeed occurred), without having to attend to cosmetic matters, and was considerate, she pointed out, of those who preferred to handle dead bodies as little as possible.

"Social death" can be said to be marked by that point at which socially relevant attributes of the patient begin permanently to cease to be operative as conditions for treating him, and when he is, essentially, regarded as already dead. "Social death" thus consists of a set of practices and can be seen to define some features of what "dying" means within the hospital context. These practices are to be distinguished from such activities as conversation in the presence of an anesthetized patient, for example, unless such conversation involves reference to the person as essentially a corpse, i.e., where the reference terms, activities discussed, and the like are those which are typically and properly discussed only with respect to persons actually dead.

It is perhaps analytically tempting to conceive of social "death" as any instance of radically asocial treatment of a person, but such a usage would be, at the same time, analytically ambiguous, permitting such things as desertion by one's family, "nonperson treatment," and the like, to be so conceived. In keeping with the literal sense of "death," I intend a more delimited sense of "dead," i.e., where death is the warrantable basis for doing such things as planning an autopsy, disposing of personal effects, contracting mortuary institutions, putting a body in the morgue, informing insurance companies, remarrying, grieving, announcing the contents of a will, preparing obituary notices, transferring properties to another name, and, generally, engaging in those organizational, ceremonial, and economic activities associated with death, those matters which mark the end of social existence. Treatments or activities which often accompany the death of a person, or his "dying," but which accompany other kinds of states as well, are not specifically instances of "social death treatment," in my terminology. So the tapering off of visits on the part of relatives becomes an instance of "treatment as dead" when those activities which are substituted for visiting are ones that would occur only after the patient had died. The distinction is not entirely without ambiguity, but within the hospital setting at least, a specific set of activities and treatments can usually be clearly located. When such activities occur, "social death" or "dying as a form of treatment" is said to occur, and whether that takes place before, concurrent with, or well after actual "biological" or "clinical" death is a matter for analysis.

A clear instance is seen in the circumstance where autopsy permits are filled out prior to death. For an autopsy to be performed, permission of the closest surviving relative must be obtained.[11] Two forms of permission constitute legally actionable documents: *1.* a signature on a prepared "autopsy permission form"[12] and *2.* a telegram from the

[11] This is apparently not true in all sections of the country. In some jurisdictions physicians can perform "limited autopsies," exploring only those areas of the body which are believed to be directly associated with the death, without obtaining permission from the family. See, for example, S. R. Cutolo, *Bellevue Is My Home* (Garden City: Doubleday & Company, Inc., 1956), p. 155. In those cases in which the coroner's office is involved in a death, no autopsy permission need be obtained.

[12] The autopsy permit reads:

I _____ bearing the relation of _____ to _____, a patient recently deceased in County Hospital, authorize the proper authorities to examine the body and head of said deceased patient and to remove organs and to retain such portions as may be considered necessary for further study to ascertain the correct cause of death.

Signed _____

Nearest Relative

surviving relative to the hospital, authorizing an autopsy. Obtaining an autopsy permit is regarded as a very important administrative necessity at the time of death. In order to qualify for AMA accreditation as a "teaching hospital," and thus to be able to offer internships and residencies, a hospital must have an autopsy rate exceeding 25 per cent, i.e., autopsies must be performed on 25 per cent or more of the hospital's deceased patients. The minimum rate is not considered sufficient and most hospitals strive for as high a rate as is possible. It is an apparently relevant question for a prospective resident to ask of the hospital: "What is your autopsy rate?" and for him partially to base his decision on where to do a residency on the basis of these rates.[13]

County's doctors are concerned to obtain autopsy permission whenever possible, in part because they can be negatively sanctioned for acting indifferently in this regard. When they expect that they will lose contact with a relative, they will, on those occasions where doing an autopsy is considered quite important (say, for example, on a particularly interesting or diagnostically troublesome case), sometimes approach the relative of a patient who is considered to be "dying" and tactfully request that, "given the circumstances," a form be signed at the present time. At County this practice was employed only in cases where an autopsy was especially desired and then only if the relative had been previously been made well aware that the patient was expected to die shortly.[14]

13   The autopsy percentage of hospital deaths reflects the degree of excellence of the medical staff. Institutions which conduct intern and resident programs should obtain an autopsy rate of 25 per cent as a minimum. The average good general hospital should aim for a minimum of 50 per cent, though some outstanding institutions obtain percentages of 70 or higher.

J. K. Owen, *Modern Concepts of Hospital Administration* (Philadelphia: W. B. Saunders Co., 1962), p. 304. Physicians have a vested interest in the over-all death rate. A hospital where few patients die is less suitable for training, whatever the percentage of autopsies. It is a high percentage of a large number of cases, providing many autopsy possibilities, that is desired. With every death, it is claimed, more experience is gained.

14 In some hospitals, however, obtaining autopsy permits before death is openly encouraged, as for example at Cook County:

One of the most important characteristics of a well regulated hospital is that it obtains as many autopsies as possible. For this the hospital depends to the largest degree on the residents and interns of the ward. They must recognize cases in which death is imminent or likely, and must make an immediate effort to advise the nearest of kin of the seriousness of the case, and to request written permit of autopsy. They must use their ingenuity in acquainting the relative with the importance of the autopsy. . . . Often in hopeless cases, the intern can succeed in obtaining a permit for a limited autopsy if he can show that it is not more than an operation.

A. Bernstein, *Intern's Manual* (*Cook County Hospital*) (Chicago: Year Book Medical Publishers, Inc., 1959), p. 190.

There is the feeling, moreover, that one can risk the possible sanctioning that a proposal might incur only with either the very uneducated relative or the very sophisticated and emotionally cool one. In the next section where I discuss the timing of "social death treatments" and proclamations of impending deaths to families, I shall consider the character of such risks.

A typical instance of "social death" involved a male patient who was admitted to the Emergency Unit with a sudden perforation of a duodenal ulcer. He was operated upon, and, for a period of six days, remained in quite critical condition. His wife was informed that his chances of survival were poor, whereupon she stopped her visits to the hospital. After two weeks, the man's condition improved markedly and he was discharged in ambulatory condition. The next day he was readmitted to the hospital with a severe coronary. Before he died, he recounted his experience upon returning home. His wife had removed all of his clothing and personal effects from the house, had made preliminary arrangements for his burial with the mortuary establishment (she had written a letter which he discovered on his bureau, requesting a brochure on their rates), she no longer wore his wedding ring, and was found with another man, no doubt quite shocked at her husband's return. He reported that he left the house, began to drink heavily, and had a heart attack.

❦ ❦ ❦ PREPARATION OF THE CORPSE AND PRE-CORPSE

A standard "death procedure" in nearly all American hospitals is the practice of "body wrapping." When a patient dies, the hospital "death procedures manual" instructs, his body is to be "wrapped" in a specially provided "Morgue Sheet." Apparently, the body wrapping activity is done nearly everywhere in U.S. hospitals in essentially the same fashion.[15]

At County, body wrapping is the work of aides and orderlies, over 95 per cent of whom are Negroes. There is a legal regulation—purportedly instituted to protect the corpse from sexual attention—requiring that nurses' aides wrap female bodies and orderlies wrap male bodies; the

[15] M. MacEachern, *Hospital Organization and Management*, 3rd edition (Chicago: Physicians Record Company, 1957), the standard source book on hospital administrative policy, gives the following as a "standing order":

Care of the Body after Death
Wash the body carefully, plug the rectum (male) and vagina (female) with cotton, tie the chin so that the mouth is closed, close the eyes, dress the body in its clothes if these are available, and if not wrap the body in a morgue sheet. A morgue basket is to be found in the central supply room.

A 34-item list of steps in the wrapping of a body is given in G. Cherescavich, *A Textbook for Nursing Assistants* (St. Louis: C. V. Mosby Co., 1964), pp. 455–457.

sexual segregation of body care found in the handling of dead bodies is thus similar to that which governs some aspects of the care of live ones. There is also a regulation, at County as elsewhere, which requires that when a female body is removed from the ward to the hospital morgue by a male attendant, a nurse must escort it, this ruling being in some ways similar to that which requires a nurse to be present when a physician conducts a vaginal examination. Neither of these two regulations is followed at County; male morgue attendants regularly transport female bodies by themselves, and male physicians do vaginal examinations without nurses being present.[16] The sex segregation of body wrapping appears to be chiefly a function of the fact that wards are segregated according to sex at County (an arrangement that does not exist at Cohen and is generally uncommon, I am told, in private hospitals), and orderlies are more commonly employed on the male wards and aides on the female wards.

Wrapping a body is a well-organized routine, having a characteristic temporal structuring: a clear beginning, sequence of steps, and closure; it is done collectively, by two or more persons, and is automatically carried off. When the technique is taught to initiates, it is taught as a complete ceremonial piece, like a variety of semiritualistic hospital routines, e.g., preparing a patient for surgery, a woman for child delivery, etc.

On any given ward there is usually a team of aides or orderlies who work together in wrapping a body. They do the task systematically, with a certain degree of finesse, and prefer to work on it with those with whom they have done it before. When a new aide or orderly is introduced to the wrapping task he is, for the first time, asked to stand by and watch, as a narrative account of the procedure is given by one of the experienced members of the team. The procedure essentially involves the complete removal of the deceased's clothing, including all jewelry, and the folding of a heavy gauge muslin sheet completely around the body, pinning it down the front with large safety pins, in mummy style. Before the body is wrapped it is occasionally cleansed with a wet cloth, not thoroughly but only to remove any particularly noticeable dirt. A diaper-like sheet is wrapped around the genital area; the hands and feet are crossed and bound together with a special cotton-covered string. Two precut gauze pads are placed over the eyes, after the lids have been closed. Before the body is finally wrapped in the outside sheet, it is checked to make sure no paraphernalia is affixed to it. All IV-tubes are removed, nasal suctioning equipment detached, catheters taken out, etc.

---

[16] An exception to this absence of concern for sexual protection is in County's Emergency Ward where, in part because of the short-term character of doctor-patient relationships and the somewhat less clearly structured contractual relationship between the parties, such examinations are always done in the presence of a nurse. In this setting doctors fear that a woman will come for an examination just to stage the circumstances for a legal suit.

In performing this task, aides or orderlies work in a coordinated fashion, indicating to the witness that the job has been done many times previously, and by the same team of workers. They start at one end of the body and work step-by-step until the procedure is finished. Typically, there is a division of labor, whereby one woman turns the body as the other spreads the sheet; this practice is institutionalized so that the same aide will typically do the same parts when working with her teammate.

The task is essentially secular in character; there are no explicit religious references made, although one aide characteristically hummed a Negro spiritual as she worked. What little talk takes place is relatively hushed in quality, and is sporadic rather than continuous. Topics are restricted to discussion of the patient, e.g., "She was a nice old woman, wasn't she?" "Yes, sure sorry to see her go"; "She was pretty sick for a long time, I think," and the like. One senior aide, every time she inserted the last safety pin in place when wrapping a body, patted the body on the thigh area and said "well, you're on your way now," whereupon she left the room. Nearly all women who have died in the female medical ward at County have received some variant of this last blessing. The whole job takes some fifteen minutes, during all of which time the workers are busy. There are no "breaks" taken in the course of the work; once begun, it is carried through to completion—with one important exception to be noted below—and when they do break they leave the room rather than take a break in the body's presence. Occasionally there is some joking, mostly about technical problems. In one instance, an aide stuck a safety pin too deeply, puncturing the skin and causing blood to appear and slightly stain the sheet. The other said, "Oh dear, guess we'll have to change the whole sheet," and the first answered, "She didn't feel nothin' though," and there was laughter.

Generally, the body is handled nonreverently by most aides and orderlies. In turning it around to wrap the sheet, it is grabbed roughly and rolled over with none of the gentleness that one observes in the rolling of live persons. One elderly nurses' aide found the generally rough treatment offensive and regularly said, throughout the course of doing a wrapping, "You shouldn't be so rough," addressing her helper, though to no great avail. Some personnel apparently take pride in the ease with which they manage what others might imagine to be the psychological discomfort of working with bodies. One aide, in demonstrating how bodies are wrapped to a new employee, took the young girl into a room where a dead patient had just been wrapped, and as she pointed to those features of the completed product which marked a good job, e.g., the sheet should be tightly fitted, she made a point of ostentatiously showing what she meant, almost hitting the body at each point to demonstrate how tightly the sheet fit.

An orderly was instructing another how to affix the identification tags bearing the patient's name, age, and sex on the feet and at the midsection of the wrapped body (these tags are the same kind one uses in parcel post, the manila variety with a double wire at the end to tie the tag on with). As the novice fumbled in trying to put the tag on gently without having its wire touch the body itself (an occurrence which to a newcomer at such activities would apparently be too close to dead flesh for comfort), the old timer looked on with a developing smile. He interrupted the sweating novice with "Here, let me show you how," and quite forcefully, with exaggerated nonchalance, jabbed the wire through the feet section, seemingly trying, on purpose, to catch some flesh on the way, and said "Don't be afraid of them, they don't feel a *thing* anymore," whereupon he laughed and the novice reciprocated with a nervous whimper.

Some parenthetical remarks about certain aspects of body care may be made here. In County, there is a clear division of labor and a clear difference in work styles with bodies. Physicians do not handle dead bodies except when they are pronouncing patients dead and conducting autopsies, and here their handling is limited strictly to the kinds of touch necessary for accomplishing these tasks. Gross body handling, e.g., movement of an entire body from one stretcher to another, from the morgue refrigerator to the autopsy table, etc., is considered so much dirty work by the doctors, and is exclusively the province of the aides and orderlies. This differentiation of touching is common in handling live bodies as well, though not so markedly so as in the case of dead ones. When performing a physical examination on a patient a doctor will, if necessary, assist in turning a patient over to place him in a better position for the examination. If several physicians of differing statuses are jointly conducting an examination, as in "rounds," senior doctors characteristically will step back and allow the junior men access to the body to aid in turning it into position. With dead bodies, interns themselves maintain a generally aloof position. Once they pronounce a patient dead, they leave the room. In the morgue, an attendant alone positions the body on the operating table, and if he has difficulty in doing so physicians do not offer assistance. Physicians here limit their physical contact with the body to that which is required for doing the postmortem as a technical activity. In surgery when a patient is being draped for an operation—an extended routine involving swabbing and the systematic laying of sheets—the junior physician of the operating team, the intern, assists nurses while superordinate physicians stand by awaiting completion of the preliminaries. In the morgue, if physicians arrive in the autopsy room before the body has been transferred there from the adjoining refrigerator room, they often leave the morgue area entirely, with an instruction for the attendant to ready

the body. They adjourn to an office and await the attendant's announcement that everything has been readied. The pathologist, on several known
occasions, scolded the attendant for not having the body prepared for
autopsy when he knew one was scheduled.

On the wards, should a nurse have need for something from the
room of a recently deceased patient, she will generally send an aide or
orderly in to secure what she needs rather than go herself, the partial
explanation apparently being that a nurse feels she has a right to keep
her proper distance from such activities as she might witness there. In
witnessing body work done on a gross level, there is a sense in which the
witness can thereby become committed to the grossness of the task, particularly so if looking on involves one in informal talk with the workers.
If one witnesses such activities silently, he can assume the status of a
mere on-looker, but in engaging in talk in the same genre as that of the
workers, he gives others the impression that he is not sufficiently concerned about maintaining the detachment his higher status requires.

The presence of the physician in scenes where there are dead bodies
interestingly shows some of the ways medical perspectives on death and
dead bodies are sustained. With the death of a patient, the physician temporarily, until the autopsy, loses any legitimate interest in the patient; his
relationship to the patient *qua* doctor is severed with the death. The general demeanor of the doctor vis-à-vis the body seems to represent disin-
terest, rather than discomfort. With death, the patient becomes like a
discharged patient, in the sense that the contractual basis for the physician's presence and interest is terminated. Any talk that occurs in the
presence of the now corpse takes on the perceived character of "socializ-
ing," in that the physician steps out of role in doing so and has nothing to
say, as it were, that can be said as a physician. His presence is no longer
warranted and the very fact of its continuation can be regarded, and
apparently is, as a progressive movement out of role and a progressive
involvement in the fact of the death as a nonmedically relevant event.
There is a sense one gets that if the body is treated at all reverentially in
the hospital, that treatment is to be seen in the way the physician seems
almost to regard himself as an intruder in the presence of the dead body.
It would be somewhat unwarranted to talk of disattention as respectful
here, and somewhat more tempting to regard it as distaste, yet one can
locate at least one source of the disattention by reference to the way a
doctor's presence is undercut by the occurrence of the death. On the basis
of his demeanor in the presence of bodies, one can locate his action there
along with his behavior in other pre- and postwork relevant involvements,
e.g., that period which precedes or follows an actual physical examination,
during which the patient is getting dressed or undressed.

Having briefly described the activity of body wrapping, let me return to the main theme, the treatment of the "dying" patient. Despite the fact that it is routinely done, body wrapping is regarded by aides and orderlies throughout the hospital as an unpleasant task, and while these personnel come to do it with no special fear, they do not, characteristically, look forward to it. In fact, they systematically attempt to avoid the task. One quite common device at County is to pretend that the patient has not died, and, if necessary and possible, try to camouflage his death by making him look alive. If they succeed, aides or orderlies can manage to pass off the body for the next shift, which, when rounds are made, will discover it and be responsible for wrapping it. The body is camouflaged by propping the head up, closing the eyes to feign the appearance of sleep, keeping intravenous solutions flowing, and screening off the body so that bypassing personnel, e.g., nurses and doctors, will not notice the dead body.

A more simple and common technique, particularly possible if the shift change will occur shortly, is to take a long coffee break, get involved in some other task, and hope that coworkers will be called upon to wrap the body. These practices may be spoken of as instances of "clinical" and "biological" death before "social death," which is a less prevalent phenomenon at County than the reverse.

The wrapping task is also handled in an opposite fashion, this being one case where it is done in stages and not as an entire piece. What occasionally occurs here is that portions of the wrapping are done before death, leaving only a few moments of final touch-up work with the dead body. This practice requires very knowledgeable personnel, those who can, with rather high accuracy, detect immediately forthcoming deaths. There is often one such person on any ward at any shift—particularly on the medical wards where an employee gains a good deal of experience in judging such matters. On the male medical ward a nurse prided herself on the "fact" that she could predict, in many cases, which patients would die within the day, if any. A short-term check by asking for her predictions each morning and checking them against actual deaths revealed that she approached a 75 per cent degree of accuracy, and in several cases predicted the deaths of patients whom doctors did not expect to die as soon as she said they would. If such a person is available and aides can learn of her expectations, or themselves are good forecasters, they will occasionally go into the room of such a patient, change the bedsheets, insert dentures, and, in several cases I know of, diaper a patient who is still "alive." Such predeath treatment is likely to occur only during the night shift, when aides are assured that relatives will not visit and discover their work. When the patient dies, aides know that doctors will not examine the feet and discover the binding (if they do, as happened in one known case, the aides gave the account "right after he died we started on him"—a practice that is not officially sanctioned before the pronouncement of death, but is ordinary operating practice). Once the patient actually dies, all that remains to do is tie the arms and wrap the entire body, the more unpleasant matters like diapering and replacing dentures having been taken care of previously. Care must be taken here too lest the bedsheets become soiled again, though that possibility can conveniently be explained to be the result of postdeath excretions.

Various other practices are designed to avoid or minimize the processing of a dead body, and these too involve predeath treatment of persons as essentially dead. A very common one entails the "improper" use of interward transfers. A patient who comes into the Emergency Ward whose condition is such that his death is expected shortly, will occasionally be transferred to a medical or surgical ward, the presumed motive being that he is terminally ill and not properly a person for emergency care. The actual motive is suspected by the receiving ward's personnel to be the removal of a patient who is about to die so as to avoid having to care for his body. One evening a patient in quite critical condition was transferred from the Emergency Ward to the men's medical ward. The head evening nurse refused to accept the obviously dying patient, and complained that the Emergency Ward clerk simply sent him over to die on her property. She angrily instructed the orderly to return the patient to the Emergency Ward, with the message, "You tell Mrs. Smith to wrap her own bodies."

A very common example of "social death" before "actual" death involves the assignment of patients to beds. A patient who is admitted to the hospital in what is considered to be a near-death state: with, for example, extremely low blood pressure, very erratic heart beats, and a nonpalpable or very weak pulse, is frequently left on the stretcher on which he is admitted and put in the laboratory room, or large supply room. In such cases, a nurse explained, they don't want to mess a bed up and, since the patient would soon die, there was no need to assign a bed (upon death, the complete bedding must be stripped, the room thoroughly cleansed, disinfected, etc.). In several cases, patients were left throughout the night to die in the supply room, and, if in the morning they were still alive, nurses quickly assigned them beds, before the arrival of physicians and/or relatives. Here we see instances of movement back and forth between the statuses of life and death, with social life, at least as represented by a bona fide admission to the hospital bed, reinstituted after a night of treatment as a corpse.

During a "death watch," the phrase used by nursing personnel to refer to guarding a dying patient in anticipation of his death, the patient is treated as in a transitory state, the relevant facts about him being the gradual decline of clinical life signs. As death approaches, his status as a *body* becomes more evident in the manner in which he is discussed, treated, and moved about. Attention shifts more and more away from caring for his possible discomforts and instituting medically advised treatments, to the sheer activity of "timing" his biological events. With a pre-death-coma patient, suctioning of the nasal passages, propping up pillows, changing bedsheets, and the like, routinely occur as part of the normal nursing routine. As blood pressure drops and signs of imminent death are taken to be apparent, these traditional nursing practices become regarded as less important and the major items of interest become the number of his heart beats and the changing condition of his eyes. Suctioning activity diminishes in frequency, his position is not so regularly altered to insure more comfort, and the surroundings are not kept in any particular state of cleanliness. On many occasions, nurses' aides were observed to cease administering standing-order oral medications when death was expected to take place within the hour.

The technical feasibility of phasing out the treatment of dying patients is enhanced by the character of the ward social structure. While "posted patients" theoretically have the right to round-the-clock visitors, in actuality nurses strive to separate relatives from those patients whose deaths are regarded as imminent. They urge family members to go home and await further news there or, at best, insist that they wait outside in the corridors and not in the patient's room. At least part of their concern in doing so is to handle the forthcoming death within the context of other ward responsibilities. It is common for a patient to die unattended and be discovered as dead only considerably later, when a nurse, aide, or doctor happens into his room. One orderly refused, for the first several weeks he was employed in the hospital, to wander in and out of rooms, as an orderly must, his fear being that he wouldn't be able to manage himself should he come upon a dead person. At County the occasion of a death is not particularly publicized on the ward, so that staff members are not always forewarned when one has occurred. On one occasion, the lack of communication on the medical wards resulted in a rather unfortunate circumstance. A woman was admitted to the female medical ward with severe vaginal bleeding. Normally, such a patient would have been taken to the obstetrics ward but in this instance there were no vacant beds on that service. In the course of her stay she delivered a stillborn, extremely malformed infant. The "baby" was wrapped in the traditional fashion and taken to the morgue. During the evening shift, an elderly woman arrived on the ward and announced that she was the "grandmother" of the deceased baby. She was quite "hysterical" and demanded to see the baby whom she claimed they "had killed." After an argumentative few moments the head nurse agreed to take her to the morgue and show the baby to her, a procedure which, she explained, was highly irregular. They went to the morgue, the nurse consulted the list of compartment "occupants," and pulled out the tray containing the stillborn. She unwrapped the sheet, exposing a horribly deformed creature, whereupon the "grandmother" fainted and badly bruised her scalp. The nurse was furious for not having been informed of the baby's condition and, trembling noticeably, ran for help. A meeting was held the next day by the medical nursing staff wherein it was agreed that thereafter every "report session" should make explicit mention of all the day's death and review any particularly relevant facts about them.

At County, relatives are present infrequently at the time of the death. After a death occurs, the family is occasionally asked, by the physician who announces the death, if they wish to view the deceased. Very few relatives request to do so, but should they, the procedure is for the body to be wrapped completely, with the exception of the head, which is to be propped up on a pillow for display. On such occasions, the hospital stages a miniature ritual. An aide combs the hair, fluffs the pillow, and otherwise tries to simulate the state of restful "repose" which morticians pride themselves in accomplishing. For at least one such aide, the hospital experience in this and related tasks served as a practical introduction to the mortuary profession, for which she left her job at the hospital to prepare.

Should relatives request to view the body, the rule is that the body be allowed to remain on the ward, prepared for viewing, for no more than an hour after death. In fact, as we have seen, bodies stay around much longer. Staging a viewing is disruptive of ward and hospital morgue activities. The body must be specially wrapped with the head remaining exposed, the nurse must go into the patient's room with the family, so as to control the possibility of an unmanageable scene, and the morgue attendant must forestall autopsy preparations. If an autopsy permit has already been signed and it is the morning when such procedures are normally performed, the morgue attendant will try to get the nurse in charge to release the body before viewing. Several occasions are known of where this occurred; when relatives arrived to view the body they were told that regulations had required that the body be removed from the floor.

Typically, however, relatives are not in the hospital at the time of the death and generally, in the greatest majority of cases, they do not request to see the "patient." Before death, with relatives continuously present in the "dying" patient's room, a more constant vigilance over the patient's condition must be maintained, this requiring, in effect, the removal of a nurse from other activities to spend her time exclusively at the bedside. The routine handling of death as it occurs on the medical wards at County requires that the ward be kept relatively free of outsiders, whose mere presence exacts greater demands on the behavior of staff than the likelihood of a death would normally warrant. Discovery, or even simultaneous discovery of the death by relative and physician, or relative and nurse, is considered as something to be avoided. While the justification for shielding off dying patients from relatives is made in terms of the "unpleasantness of seeing someone die," the fact that such shielding does not always occur in other kinds of hospitals (like Cohen, where relatives are considered specially entitled to be present at the bedside when the patient "expires") seems to point to the character of hospital routines in these different settings and the organization of "death care" as the crucial basis for this practice. At County, predeath body treatment can occur as it does only if family members are kept away, and a phasing out of attention is allowable so long as the family cannot witness or infer it.

The physician, too, at County prefers that relatives be kept away from the bedside of a dying patient, so that he is free to leave the bedside himself and attend to other matters. This concern operates particularly strongly during late evening hours, when the sheer fact of a dying patient on his service would not ordinarily require his continuous presence. With respect to most of his "dying" patients, the physician regards the forthcoming death matter of factly and feels no special discomfort in the fact that no one is actually on hand when it takes place. The absence of relatives on the ward, and especially at the bedside, allows him to wait until a more reasonable hour to come to the ward to pronounce a patient dead and then inform the relatives of the death. In many instances a patient is discovered dead in the midst of the night and the doctor not informed of the death until the morning. Physicians often express anger at nurses who awaken them at night because of the death of one of their patients.[17] It routinely happens then that a patient will die while a doctor is not on the ward and remain "unpronounced" until the physician finds it suitable and convenient to come in. The absence of relatives at close proximity to the bedside further allows nurses to avoid calling the doctor in charge until they themselves are about to leave the shift. This way they can assist their aide staff in passing on the body for the next shift. One of the disadvantages of the daytime shift from

[17] This annoyance has been noted by other observers. For example, K. R. Eissler, *op. cit.*, p. 42, notes:

> . . . I have noticed in a few instances that dying may be conceived of as a malicious act performed for the sake of annoying others. One physician complained bitterly that most of his fatal patients died at night and that he had to get up to sign their death certificates. There was no doubt that he had the fantasy that patients could have died at a different time had they not meant to annoy him.

the perspective of nurses and aides is the greater likelihood of having to remove several bodies upon their arrival at work. They themselves find it less easy to pass a body on, as it were, to the evening shift, given the greater activity of the daytime shift, the movement back and forth of patients and doctors, the need for bedspace for new admissions, etc., and thus the greater likelihood of discovering a body and the greater difficulty of concealing one. Of course, the nighttime shift cannot pass over every body to the day shift, because it quickly becomes obvious that not all nighttime deaths occur after 6:30 A.M. Some effort is made to randomize the recorded death times, but the night shift always manages to get away with fewer bodies to wrap than any other shift, even though the distribution of reported deaths, by hours, is apparently random over the long run.

Discovering a dead patient typically occurs in the course of on-going ward activity. Most patients die unattended at County, largely because of the nature of the care accorded them when they reach what is considered to be the "dying" stage. In encountering those patients whose death is considered imminent, experienced personnel manifest a characteristic stance of caution, lest the patient already be dead and that fact not noticed. As nurses make their rounds, they periodically check up on "dying patients." That check involves a long stare from the door to see if the patient is breathing (some middle-class mothers are known to do the same with their new infants, but the basis for this seems quite different in the two cases). The nurse's chief concern is to detect death shortly after it occurs so as to institute proper preparations to remove the body from the ward quickly and in so doing insure that her subordinate personnel do not neglect their responsibilities. While aides seek to avoid making such discoveries, in part because of the fact that they are the ones directly implicated in the body's care, most nurses, with the exception of a few alienated ones, are concerned to insure that such discoveries are promptly made.

It is considered relatively disastrous for a young student nurse unwittingly to treat a dead person as though he were still alive, yet on several occasions newer personnel have had such experiences. In one case a man was being attended who had been severely burned and was almost totally wrapped in gauze, with the exception of his eyes. A young student spent several minutes trying to get him to drink some juice through a straw. Having no success, she reported to her instructor for help. The instructor said, "Well, honey, of course he won't respond, he's been dead for twenty minutes." When the student gathered herself together she explained that all she "could see was his eyes and they had always been closed." Another young student, carefully following her routines from bedside to bedside, spent several moments chang-

ing the bedsheets of a patient who had just died. Another carefully
suctioned the nasal passages of a deceased patient. Still another gave a
deceased patient an injection. For one who is even slightly experienced
in witnessing and handling the dead, the likelihood of such occurrences
seems quite rare. However, it is apparently the case that unless one
realizes that he might be handling a dead person, death's occurrence
may go unnoticed, the more so it seems as the procedure one performs is
done in a perfunctorily routine manner. Such occasions are regarded seriously and not usually taken as warranting humor. The student nurse who
was told the patient she had just injected was already dead cried nervously and trembled for several minutes; she was given a half-hour off to
recover from her distress.

While such occurrences are empirically uncommon, their possibility
seems somewhat enhanced by the fact that the general notion of "being
in a coma" operates as it does. So-called "comatose" patients are treated
as essentially dead. Considering a person in a coma is warrant for talking
about him in his "presence" in ways that would not be permissible were
he awake (perhaps this distinguishes the comatose- and anesthetized-
person treatment from true "nonperson treatment," i.e., treatment of a
person as not present even though he is sensibly on the scene and capable
of monitoring what goes on conversationally).[18]

There is apparently some question as to whether verbal interchange
is accessible or not to the "comatose" patient, for some such patients—
those who live through the "coma"—are known to have reported scat-
tered detail of things said in their presence.[19] In County, however,
the "coma" is considered equivalent to general anesthesia in its effects,
and patients' conditions and prospects are freely discussed in their
presence when they are felt to be comatose. Such an assessment is
made when the patient does not respond to verbal or physical stimuli,
and the possibility that nonresponsiveness may be an inability to respond
to, rather than receive, stimulation, is not seriously entertained.

In dealing with comatose patients—a high proportion of County's
critically ill population—personnel became accustomed to disattending
the patient as a social object, so much so that the fact that the patient might

[18] For a discussion of "nonperson" treatment see E. Goffman, *Presentation of Self in
Everyday Life* (Garden City: Doubleday & Company, Inc., 1959), pp. 151–152.
[19] Formally, at least, nurses are instructed in textbooks:

Nothing should be said in the room that he should not hear, for no one
knows how much the seemingly unconscious person can hear. Whispering
especially should be avoided. The patient may see the lips move and be
distressed that he cannot hear what is said.

B. Harmer, *Textbook of the Principles and Practice of Nursing*, 5th edition (New
York: The Macmillan Company, 1955), p. 933. See also, E. Meyers, "Nursing the
Comatose Patient," *American Journal of Nursing*, 54, 716–718.

already be dead may occasionally slip by unnoticed. Since predeath treatment as a corpse extends backward in time to include many comatose patients, there is, in actual practice, little distinction between the comatose and the dead. A patient "dies," in some important organizational respects, once he enters what is taken to be a terminal coma; and death itself is not radically marked by a special attitude toward the body, or at least as much so as that which it evokes when it occurs "suddenly," with no transitory period of "dying in a coma." Far and above the greatest number of deaths that occur at County, and at Cohen, are deaths that are preceded by a period generally regarded as a coma. Of some 200 deaths observed, no deaths of the Hollywood version, wherein the person's last sentence is interrupted by his final breath, have been observed.[20]

The noncomatose patient who is expected to die on the current hospital admission cannot be the object of predeath treatment as a corpse until the coma itself is entered. In these patients' presence, that talk about their prospects which occurs is camouflaged by the use of a special descriptive language that it is assumed the patient cannot decipher. In the presence of a woman who was expected within a week to die of uremic poisoning, one physician said to a nurse, "She'll probably terminate this week." The patient, a very anxious Negro woman who may have detected the relative somberness of the physician's mood and the general seriousness of her state, nervously asked, "Am I all right, doctor?" and the physician answered, "Yes, Mrs. K., you're doing just fine."

[20] . . . the classical deathbed scene, with its loving partings and solemn last words, is practically a thing of the past; in its stead is a sedated, comatose, betubed object, manipulated and subconscious, if not subhuman.

From J. Fletcher, "The Patient's Right to Die," *Harper's*, **221** (October, 1960), 141.
It is to be noted that the "Hollywood version," as a production, can be reproduced in actual circumstances, despite the comatose situation, when persons are assembled at the bedside to await the final breath. The absence of this sort of scene can be regarded, partially at least, as a consequence of the lack of such production as much as a consequence of the way "death occurs." It is interesting that arguments for euthanasia rest heavily upon claiming that mercy killings will end the life of a "vegetable" which, it is argued, does not seem worth preserving. If one regards that "vegetable" life as a consequence of social arrangements (and, perhaps, the use of heavy sedations in the first place), then it would seem equally plausible to suggest that rather than euthanasia, what is needed is to let the death be the death of a live man and not a vegetable. Those who propose the "honorable death" supposedly have this alternative in mind, as Orwell, who says it is best not to die in a hospital at all. The "need" for euthanasia seems to be a direct consequence of the patterns of care and regard for pain which modern medical practice has institutionalized. L. Wertenbaker's *Death of a Man* (London: William Heinemann, Limited, 1957) portrays a vivid example of a man who refused to be placed in a position where euthanasia might be a relevant consideration by fighting his cancer to its end outside of the hospital.

❦ ❦ ❦ PROGNOSTICATIONS OF DYING

Thus far I have discussed some of the procedures which "dying" at County can be said to consist of. These involve treatment of patients as essentially dead where anticipation of their deaths on a given hospital admission warrants; the gradual preparation, on occasions where the patient is considered "comatose," of his body for removal to the hospital morgue; and, in the case of some patients, the lack of any bona-fide admission to the ward in the first place. It is to be kept in mind that since County is an acute treatment hospital, the average length of stay is less than ten days. This means that of the patients who die in the hospital, quite a few have never engaged in social interaction with doctors and nurses, or their family members, during the course of this final hospital admission. Unlike the circumstance of long-term chronic care facilities, or in private institutions where patients can afford prolonged treatment and where physicians have a greater stake in the outcomes of their patients' illnesses, at County Hospital patients are discharged from the hospital as soon as they show capability of being able to make it on their own.[21] It is hard-and-fast policy to keep the patient population circulating as much as possible. While the hospital stay for a heart attack victim at Cohen Hospital frequently exceeds four weeks, the same kind of patient will seldom spend more than 12 days at County, even though he may be back in the hospital many more times in the course of a year than the Cohen patient.

Of some 200 deaths witnessed, only a dozen or so involved patients who had had previous interaction with the members of the hospital staff in the course of their final hospital admission; all the rest were "far enough along" in their illnesses to be in "comatose" condition from the time of entry into the hospital up until their deaths. The greatest proportion of deaths occur within three days after the person's admission to the hospital.

The timing of proclamations of "dying," or "terminality"—both those made among staff members to each other and to the families of patients—is more or less crucial depending upon the way those who make such proclamations, or undertake treatment on the basis of an expectation of death-this-time, have their activities scrutinized by others, including the family.[22] Before a body will be "prewrapped," before it

[21] A partial rationale for this practice, over and above the stated reasons of "economy" and "the need to serve as many as possible," was suggested in Chapter 1 as the concern to keep a medically interesting population of patients on hand.

[22] For discussions of the timing of prognostications in other settings, see F. Davis, "Uncertainty in Medical Prognosis," *American Journal of Sociology* (July, 1960), 41–47, and J. Roth, *Timetables* (Indianapolis: The Bobbs-Merrill Co., Inc., 1963), Chapters I and II. For a discussion of the tenuous position of the physician at the

will be kept overnight in a treatment room rather than be assigned to a bed, before autopsy permission will be sought prior to death, ward personnel must feel as though they have quite firm reason to believe the patient's death is extremely close in coming. "Dying," as such procedures, awaits the final moments.

Yet the notion of "dying" extends beyond such forms of treatment, i.e., body treatments per se, to include the relevance or not of instituting treatments to forestall death. Noncurative treatment, which can be assembled under the general heading of "palliative care" (or "terminal care" as it is sometimes called), is to be distinguished from what is generally spoken of as "enthanasia" which, in its typical conception, involves the purposeful termination of life through some active intervention so as to shorten a painful period of dying.[23] Instances of this "pure-form" euthanasia were not found at County or Cohen. But "palliative care," negatively defined by the admitted suspension of curative medical treatments and positively by the admitted concern to treat pain only, i.e., symptomatically, is commonplace at County when persons are expected to die during a given hospital admission. The institution of "palliative care" is one important practical consequence of regarding a patient as "terminally ill" at County; and insofar as the suspension of curative medical treatments—or treatments designed to prolong life—may have as an effect the shortening of life, then the conception of the patient as "dying," operating to warrant this care, may take on the character of a "self-fulfilling prophecy," to use a familiar phrase.

From the physician's standpoint, a case ceases to be medically interesting in the comatose, predeath stage. Once "palliative care" is instituted, diagnostic enthusiasm becomes less sustainable. The care of such patients is considered as essentially a matter for nursing personnel, and physicians lose their interest in the patient. When that point is reached where the likelihood of an improvement of condition is considered negligible, the activities of diagnosis and consequent treatment lose, for the intern and/or resident in training, one of their key functions, namely, their ability to allow him to demonstrate his technical competencies and engage in semiexperimental learning ventures.

No matter how firmly grounded in experience the physician's assessment of inevitable death within specifiable time periods, no matter

time of death, see W. L. Warner, *The Living and the Dead* (New Haven: Yale University Press, 1959), pp. 310–314.
[23] There is a large literature on the subject of euthanasia, most of which treats inherent definitional difficulties. See particularly, G. Williams, *The Sanctity of Life and the Criminal Law* (New York: Alfred A. Knopf, Inc., 1957), pp. 311–350, J. Fletcher, *Morale and Medicine* (Princeton: Princeton University Press, 1954), pp. 178–190, and N. St. John-Stevas, *Life, Death and the Law* (New York: Meridian Books, 1961), Chapter 7, pp. 262–281.

how deteriorated and beyond repair the patient's condition, the reluctance or hesitancy or willingness to orient to the patient as one who is dying can often be located by reference to the pressures that confront the physician, and particularly by reference to the extent and manner in which he finds his activities accountable to others. Within the course of a hospital admission that is felt to be the patient's last, the timing of the proclamation—or if not an outright proclamation then the institution of "merely palliative care"—can be seen as largely a function of the various audiences that the physician faces and attends as audiences he might be obliged to face.

In the course of their daily business physicians engage in premising medical courses of action on the basis of diagnostic and prognostic assessments of the patient's medically defined circumstances. They are held to account, or potentially held to account, within the organized medical profession by rules of certification, within the hospital by the sanctioning mechanisms available to their superiors, peers, and subordinates, and by the public through the resources of the legal system and mechanisms of public opinion and preferences, for the competencies they demonstrate in programming courses of treatment. The occurrence of a physician's patient's death can often be a key focal point for considering the operation of these varying sanctioning systems.

The ideal circumstance of death, from the physician's standpoint, is death resulting from "dying" when "dying" means the operation of some locatable "fatal process" that can be prospectively, i.e., not after the death, properly spoken of as the thing "which will cause it." The ability of the physician to "discover dying," as this "process" and prospectively announce that discovery, provides him with a way of locating the "cause" of the death so that he can disclaim his own personal responsibility (and the responsibility of the medical discipline) for the death.

The least comfortable circumstance of death, from the doctor's perspective, is when it occurs where there has been no predictive statement of its possibility in advance. Here the physician is in the situation of having possibly to confront accusations of his own incompetence. These accusations, in turn, may establish the conditions under which he, rather than a disease's inevitable, natural operation, can potentially be considered as material in the occurrence of the death.

A central concern of the physician is his attempt to minimize the likelihood of the latter variety of death by providing, wherever possible, that relevant others will regard death as always possible, even though no specific basis for its possibility, i.e., a disease or other causally adequate and appropriate category, is located. While seeking to institutionalize something of a general air of pessimism, at the same time the physician must be careful not to convey to others the sense that in regarding death's likelihood thusly he is adopting a seemingly fatalistic stance toward recovery and the success of treatment. An important category for him to establish as a way in which others will attend his activities by way of the patient's performance is "possibly dying." The character of the language of medical prognosis can be analyzed as partially structured to establish the relevance of that category.

County physicians continuously concern themselves with having their prognostic conversations with patients' relatives convey a proper degree of solemnity. The general problem can be posed as follows: The physician must attempt to describe the patient's condition in such a way that, in the event of death, the family retrospectively will regard his own activities and attitude as having been warranted. The physician who tells the members of his patient's family that there is likely to be a death can find himself in the uncomfortable situation of having to re-encounter them on each of a series of successive days with much the same news, despite the fact that the patient continues to live. Unless the doctor has fairly sure expectations that death is immediately forthcoming, he will not employ "dying" as a way of posing the patient's condition, out of a concern that the patient, in living for a longer period of time than he expects, will provide relatives with a basis for saying the doctor made and acted upon a premature estimation of forthcoming and inevitable death; that had he treated the patient with an eye toward effecting a cure, death might not have occurred. Proclamations of inevitable death must thus be made at a well-timed point, unless it were the case that "dying" could be proposed as a reversible process. It seems to be the case that persons attend the notion "dying," in County at least, as a description of a state of affairs that is nonpreventable. That is, once personnel use the term, they intend by it to point to the expectation that death will occur within the course of the present admission. If they intend to point to a situation of possible death they employ other terms.

On several occasions, premature proclamations of inevitable death resulted in embarrassing situations. An intern informed a group of sons and daughters that their father was "dying" and the father continued to live for over a week. Each day, a large family of sons, daughters, grandchildren, nieces, and nephews came to visit the patient, and each member of the family took turns going into his room to have a last look at "papa." A son served as a ritual leader each evening, standing outside the door to the room and scheduling the visits so that each member of the family would have his turn. This went on for several days, and, as time progressed, the finality of their visits became questionable. Those relatives who had made what they thought to be a final farewell found themselves returning to the hospital and re-entering the room again and again; soon the ritual seemed to degenerate through a lack of closure. On the sixth day, the son asked to see another physician and, it was reported, offered a cautiously voiced complaint because it seemed to him that his father was indeed not dying, yet apparently being treated as though he were. The intern was advised by his superiors of the tactlessness of his premature announcement to the family. Because things had stretched out a bit too long, he had provided for the relevance of predeath bereavement when it wasn't apparently relevant. "Fortunately," perhaps, for the intern, the man died on the seventh night in the hospital.[24]

It is worth suggesting, though no data is specifically available on the matter, that one of the physician's concerns in making prognostications of death is to structure them so that the family will not, by beginning to regard the patient as "already dead" and taking appropriate preparatory measures, begin to experience a sense of guilt when death does not occur in a reasonable amount of time. To the extent that a prognosis of upcoming death is proposed and taken as the warrantable basis for beginning to "adjust" to the "facts of life," a danger is always present that this warrant will be undercut if the prognosis is prematurely made and preparations proceed too rapidly. I have noticed that when physicians make such proclamations they do so in such a manner as to be nondirective regarding the steps that families ought to begin to take, allowing relatives to assess their own responsibilities in that regard and leaving upon them the burden of guilt should they prepare with inappropriately early vigor and enthusiasm. Prognostic conversations between County physicians and the relatives of seriously ill patients are characterized by the doctor's saying little, taking his cues as to what to provide in the way of information, advice, etc., from the questions relatives ask. The doctor tries to detect how much the relatives want to hear and adjusts his portrayals of the patient's condition to what he expects relatives seek to understand under their concerns for knowing how to behave with respect to the patient.

Not only do vigorousness and enthusiasm exist as modes in which preparations for an expected death occur, by survivors-to-be, but so does that mode of preparation which has its purported impact in the sense that with death coming, appropriate solemnity should be established in the behavior of the survivors-to-be. In the case of famous persons, for example, bereavement often begins prior to the death itself; while the great are "dying" certain circles of activity may come to a standstill, and the manner of mourning may come to be an appropriate manner of

[24] See Glaser and Strauss, "Awareness Contexts and Social Interaction," *op. cit.*, p. 54, for a reported similar instance.

regard for the fact of the "dying" and not simply the "death which will come." When the death doesn't shortly come, some of the import is taken out of such decent respect for the "dying," in part perhaps because respect for the "dying" seems premised on the expectation of near death, and in being overly and prematurely respectful, persons can give others, as well as themselves, the sense that they are looking forward to the "death." A sense of embarrassment can attend a ritual which begins too early, just as one which begins too late, or never at all. The propriety of exhibiting solemnity for too long can become strained, particularly if persons are so situated in the social structure that they can get the feeling that they ought really to be back at their businesses, not having the right to grieve so protractedly. In Chapter 6 I shall discuss the "right to grieve" in more detail. The recent case of Churchill's death seems from some reports to be a good example of this sort of uneasiness.[25]

Just as proclamations of inevitable death must not be made too prematurely, they must also not be made too close to the point of the death, for then, with death following quickly after the expectation of it, the physician has less time in which to transfer the patient's fate from the world of medicine and his own hands, to those of "God." Death must be made to seem an outcome of "dying," as an inevitable transitory status, for without such a transition, death loses its apparent naturalness and becomes open to interpretation as a wrongly caused affair. A striking instance of planned sequencing was reported to have occurred in the operating room. A patient was operated upon for a gunshot wound which apparently was not considered serious enough to warrant preparing the family for the prospect of possible death. He died on the operating table, and rather than deliver the news of the death forthrightly, the operating team was reported to have decided to create a sense that "dying" preceded death by filtering out news of progressive deterioration in the patient's condition, after in fact he had already died. On each of several occasions, a member of the team encountered awaiting family members with increasingly less hopeful news of the operation's progress and the patient's health. After several progressively

---

[25] Over the course of the nine days that elapsed between the announcement of Churchill's stroke and expected death on January 16, 1965, and his actual death on the 24th, the crowds awaiting final word gradually dwindled in size, until only a handful were remaining. The entire governmental machinery in England ground to a halt and by the eighth day, editorials appeared in London newspapers criticizing high officials who had cancelled major diplomatic engagements pending Churchill's demise. *The New York Times* carried running daily accounts on Churchill's progress toward death. On January 23, p. 2, the *London Daily Mirror* was reported, by *The Times,* to have tactfully said:

  . . . is it not somehow off-key that the illness of our greatest man of action should become, for the noblest of motives, a cause of inaction and delay.

more solemn prognostications, the occurrence of death was announced, now placed within a history of "dying."

In the circumstance of DOA deaths, in the Emergency Ward, doctors who announce the death often do so in such a way as to suggest that "dying" preceded it, e.g., by saying, "Well, apparently your husband had a bad heart attack this morning and that was probably something he was predisposed to have," or "From the looks of things he was in bad condition in the past . . . ," etc. This is a situation where accountability is realistically minimized, for the doctor does not know the "patient" nor the relatives; yet even here, doctors feel obliged to suggest a natural sequence of prefatory illness. I shall look in detail at the form of "announcements of death" in Chapter 5.

Physicians generally seek to avoid the necessity of such frantic, last minute historicizing by providing that form of prognostic account which will leave open the possibility of death without directly suggesting it and thereby risking the interpretation in their actions of a premature pessimism. This is typically accomplished through gradual shifts in the tone of prognosis, whereby the attempt is made to keep open the various contingencies which might occur, never making a definite commitment. The progressive solemnization of prognostic accounts as the patient's condition deteriorates goes as follows: on early days of admission of the patient who is considered as a possible eventual death, he is talked of as "in serious condition"; as his death becomes considered more immediately imminent, references to its being "a matter of time" are made. References to "dying" are cautiously made—and only when the final moments are considered at hand. The use of such phrases as "only time will tell," "we've done all we can," "it's just a matter of waiting to let nature take its course," "there's no telling now," etc., provide that should the patient die, "dying" will have been seen as having gone on beforehand. At the same time, should the patient live through the admission, the doctor's competence is not thrown into question, but perhaps enhanced. It is always to the physician's advantage to portray the situation as slightly more serious than he feels it is, so long as its seriousness is not taken or proposed as a warrant for treating "palliatively."

The structure of County Hospital's pattern of family visiting and its typical population of relatives provide an organizational basis for handling some of the problems by structuring prognostic talk. One fact of relevance is that relatives are infrequently present in the hospital, so that, quantitatively speaking, there is little contact between physician and relative. A goodly number of County's patients are without families or have families only nominally but not actually, i.e., not responsibly. In County, as apparently in other such lower-class institutions, accountability vis-à-vis the family is not seriously attended by physicans. With a lack of historical involvement among physician, patient, and relative, the hospital is not regarded, either by members of lower-class society or by the hospital staff, as an arena to which the traditional doctor-patient relationship moves from the office. "Going to the hospital," in lower-class society, seems to mean giving oneself up to the care of an institution: it is not viewed as another step continuous with other modes of medical care. Many County patients have no "private physicians." When in the hospital, patients are, as I have noted above, treated by many doctors who interchange with one another in caring for their needs. Seeking a physician to learn of a relative's physical condition is frustrating, in that a physician often cannot be located. The doctor one sees one day is "off duty" the next. Situations of accountability are thus infrequent, both by virtue of the way relatives are generally regarded by house staff and the way County's clientele and families regard the experience of hospitalization.

At Cohen Hospital, the average morning round of the physician will involve him in repeated and oftentimes lengthy encounters with family members who request, and to whom he feels obliged to give, rather detailed accounts of patients' progress. The management of prognostic conversation here is more sensitively attended. At County, the physician may go several days without meeting a patient's relatives. Solemn forecasting at County is proposed, by staff, to result oftentimes in the family's tapering off visits to the hospital. The physician at County seeks to detect what a prognosis will mean for the relatives and will often be less hesitant to offer what might be a prematurely fatal prognosis if he feels that in doing so, he is providing relatives with a warrant for deserting the patient. The interchangeability of physicians, as a major organizational fact, provides any given doctor with the ability to underplay the likelihoods of what any given encounter with a family member will entail in the way of future encounters. Physicians hold very tightly to the view that they receive patients at the last stages of illness; that County is essentially a last resort as a treatment institution; that had the patient been properly cared for during his life, seen doctors regularly, etc., his current care could be better grounded in knowledge; that the histories they have "on patients" are notably insufficient as bases for thorough medical treatment; etc. They have developed and daily refer to their major ideology that "given all this, they can only do what is humanly possible." They often hold out little in the way of promises and use the fact of a lack of proper doctor-patient history as warranting a general degree of pessimism, which they convey in their conversations with families, regularly pointing to the fact that "most of the damage has already been done." The patient who arrives in the hospital in a semicomatose state is seldom treated as a bona-fide patient. Doctors seek to provide for the nonaccountability of their actions vis-à-vis members of the public by elaborately employing a deprecating posture about the "county hospital" state of affairs, and by generally adopting a nonenthusiastic stance—which they warrant by reference to patterns of medical care among "such patients"—they provide for their own nonaccountability in their interactions with family members. When patients die at County, doctors routinely point to the features of the care patterns in the county to locate the "cause" of the death, in a general sense, outside and over and above their own limited involvement in the health affairs of "their patients." In their daily interaction with families (which are seldom "daily"), they seek to avoid making reassurances, conveying instead their general disaffiliation from "this kind of medicine." Doctor-relative encounters have the character of so many bureaucratic-like interactions which lower-class persons confront in the various welfare agencies, e.g., that "Well, we'll do what we can" character.

It is not infrequent to find the relative, in the manner in which he asks for information, providing the sense that whatever news is given will serve as the basis for the allocation of time for visits members of the family will make. One man each day over the course of several days greeted the physician who was attending his wife with, "Is she getting worse, doctor?" and, in response to whatever the doctor said, replied, "You think it would be OK for me to leave the hospital and come back later, doctor?" The intern stated that he took this form of query as evidence of some guilt, and that he was sure that the man was awaiting a "doctor's word" to serve as a "go ahead." When the doctor told him, on the third day of his wife's admission to the hospital, "I think you can go now, there's nothing more we can do but wait and she doesn't know if you're here anyhow," the man left the hospital and never returned. His wife died two days later and he couldn't be reached, a fact which the doctor cited as evidence for the nonconcern of family members "among such people."

The general pattern of relative visiting, the interchangeability of personnel, the lack of doctor-patient-relative relationship, serve to allow the institution of "palliative care" and the enforcement of an attitude of inevitability at an early stage in the admission of a semicomatose or comatose patient. That a patient initially considered to be "dying" might survive a given admission, is less a potential source of embarrassment and potential sanctioning to the extent that relatives are not around to inquire daily into their relatives' progress. In a medical conference, a case was raised that illustrates one way in which accountability is regarded as a constraint upon premature remission of serious diagnostic attention and curative treatment. A woman was admitted to the hospital in a very weak condition with what were described as complaints of listlessness, nausea, fever, and severe loss of weight. She was 77 years old and had a history of recurrent diabetic difficulties and one previous heart attack. It was suspected, on the basis of a preliminary blood test, that she had developed a lymphosarcoma which may have been involved in a more extended cancerous development. In the course of the conference a decision had to be made as to whether or not to perform an extended series of tests to solve what was presented as a rather ambiguous diagnostic situation. One physician argued that he was convinced a diagnosis of "leukemia" was warranted, and was prepared to make a prognosis of forthcoming death on that basis. Another felt less secure about that diagnosis and argued for a more complete series of tests and the temporary suspension of further treatment until a more specific diagnosis was obtained. The family's stake in learning of the illness was then discussed. After learning that the woman's husband visited her only once during the period of the week in which she had been hospitalized, and that he had been drunk at that time, it was agreed that, since she was so "sick," and that her diabetes was acting up again, it "didn't pay," as one of them put it, to bother with the additional tests. They decided to wait and see what happened for several days, to see if she became markedly worse, and if nothing happened then to order more tests. The fact of her husband's absence was stated to be a chief consideration for not rushing to make a diagnosis. His lack of concern was admittedly taken to warrant theirs, at least to the extent that she would first be allowed to deteriorate further, if she would, before more extensive diagnostic work was pursued. If she got worse and approached death, they agreed, then there would be no point in worrying more about the diagnosis. If she didn't become more ill, they would wait to see that development, and then attempt to uncover a more secure diagnostic basis for instituting treatment.

This situation of choice, i.e., whether or not to take full efforts to treat quickly or adopt a "wait and see" attitude, is extremely common in the "care" of those patients who are regarded as potential candidates for the week's tally of deceased patients. The "wait and see" attitude is deemed legitimate by County's interns and residents when there is reason to believe that death is a distinct possibility. It prolongs the need for extensive diagnostic attention which, with these patients, is considered warranted only if they are so located in the age and social structure that life is considered especially worth preserving. I shall now examine the role of deemed social worth in programming medical courses of action and talking of "dying" and "death" by considering the circumstance of the "DOA" patient, for it is here that certain such decisional matters are rather clearly delineated.

❧ ❧ ❧ DEATH, USES OF A CORPSE, AND SOCIAL WORTH

In County's Emergency Ward, the most frequent variety of death is what is known as the "DOA" type. Approximately 40 such cases are processed through this division of the hospital each month. The designation "DOA" is somewhat ambiguous insofar as many persons are not physiologically *dead upon arrival,* but are nonetheless classified as having been such. A person who dies within several hours after having been brought to the hospital might, if upon arrival he was initially announced, by the ambulance driver, to be dead, retain such a classification at the time he is so pronounced by the physician.

When an ambulance driver suspects that the person he is carrying is dead, he signals the Emergency Ward with a special siren alarm as he approaches the entrance driveway. As he wheels his stretcher past the clerk's desk, he restates his suspicion with the remark, "possible," a shorthand reference for "Possible DOA" (the use of the term *possible* is required by law which insists, primarily for insurance purposes, that any diagnosis unless made by a certified physician be so qualified). The clerk records the arrival in a log book and pages a physician, informing him, in code, of the arrival. Often a page is not needed as physicians on duty hear the siren alarm and expecting the arrival wait at the entranceway. The "person" is rapidly wheeled to the far end of the ward corridor and into the nearest available foyer or room, supposedly out of sight of other patients and possible onlookers from the waiting room. The physician arrives, makes his examination, and pronounces the patient dead, or not. A nurse then places a phone call to the coroner's office, which is legally responsible for the removal and investigation of all DOA cases.

Neither the hospital nor the physician has medical responsibility in such cases. In many instances of clear death, ambulance drivers use the hospital as a depository because it has the advantages of being both closer and less bureaucratically complicated a place than the downtown coroner's office for disposing of a body. Here, the hospital stands as a temporary holding station, rendering the community service of legitimate and free pronouncements of death for any comers. In circumstances of near-death, it functions more traditionally as a medical institution, mobilizing life-saving procedures for those for whom they are still of potential value, at least as judged by the ER's staff of residents and interns. The boundaries between near-death and sure death are not however, as we shall shortly see, altogether clearly defined.

In nearly all DOA cases, the pronouncing physician (commonly that physician who is the first to answer the clerk's page or spot the incoming ambulance) shows, in his general demeanor and approach to the task, little more than passing interest in the event's possible occurrence and the patient's biographical and medical circumstances. He responds to the clerk's call, conducts his examination, and leaves the room once he has made the necessary official gesture to an attending nurse (the term "kaput," murmured in differing degrees of audibility depending upon the hour and his state of awakeness, is a frequently employed announcement). It happened on numerous occasions, especially during the midnight-to-eight shift, that a physician was interrupted during a coffee break to pronounce a DOA and returned to his colleagues in the canteen with, as an account of his absence, some version of "Oh, it was nothing but a DOA."

It is interesting to note that while the special siren alarm is intended to mobilize quick response on the part of the ER staff, it occasionally operates in the opposite fashion. Some ER staff came to regard the fact of a DOA as decided in advance; they exhibited a degree of nonchalance in answering the siren or page, taking it that the "possible DOA" most likely is "D." In so doing they in effect gave authorization to the ambulance driver to make such assessments. Given that time lapse which sometimes occurs between that point at which the doctor knows of the arrival and the time he gets to the patient's side, it is not inconceivable that in several instances patients who might have been revived died during this interim. This is particularly likely in that, apparently, a matter of moments may differentiate the reviveable state from the irreversible one.

Two persons in "similar" physical condition may be differentially designated dead or not. For example, a young child was brought into the ER with no registering heartbeat, respirations, or pulse—the standard "signs of death"—and was, through a rather dramatic stimulation procedure involving the coordinated work of a large team of doctors and nurses, revived for a period of eleven hours. On the same evening, shortly after the child's arrival, an elderly person who presented the same physical signs, with what a doctor later stated, in conversation, to be no discernible differences from the child in skin color, warmth, etc., "arrived" in the ER and was almost immediately pronounced dead, with no attempts at stimulation instituted. A nurse remarked, later in the evening: "They (the doctors) would never have done that to the old lady (i.e., attempt heart stimulation) even though I've seen it work on them too." During the period when emergency resuscitation equipment was being readied for the child, an intern instituted mouth-to-mouth resuscitation. This same intern was shortly relieved by oxygen machinery and when the woman "arrived," he was the one who pronounced her dead. He reported shortly afterwards that he could never bring himself to put his mouth to "an old lady's like that."

It is therefore important to note that the category "DOA" is not
totally homogeneous with respect to actual physiological condition. The
same is generally true of all deaths, the determination of *death* involving,
as it does, a critical decision, at least in its earlier stages. There is currently a movement in progress in some medical and lay circles to undercut the traditional distinction between "biological" and "clinical" death,
and procedures are being developed and their use encouraged for
treating any "clinically dead" person as potentially reviveable.[26] Should
such a movement gain widespread momentum (and it, unlike late 19th-
century arguments for life after death, is legitimated by modern medical
thinking and technology), it would foreseeably have considerable consequence for certain aspects of hospital social structure, requiring, perhaps, that much more continuous and intensive care be given "dying"
and "dead" patients than is presently accorded them, at least at County
(at Cohen Hospital, where the care of the "tentatively dead" is always

[26] There is a large popular and scientific literature developing on efforts to "treat
the dead," the import of which is to undercut traditional notions of the non-
reversibility of death. Some of this discussion goes so far as to propose the preser-
vation of corpses in a state of nondeterioration until such time as medical science
will be able to do complete renovative work. See particularly R. Ettinger, *The Prospect of Immortality* (Garden City: Doubleday & Company, Inc., 1964). The Soviet
literature on resuscitation is most extensive. Soviet physicians have given far
more attention to this problem than any others in the world. For an extensive
review of the technical literature, as well as a discussion of biomedical principles,
with particular emphasis on cardiac arrest, see V. A. Negovskii, *Resuscitation and
Artificial Hypothermia* (New York: Consultants Bureau Enterprises, Inc., 1962). See
also, L. Fridland, *The Achievement of Soviet Medicine* (New York: Twayne Publishers, Inc., 1961), especially Chapter 2, "Death Deceived," pp. 56–75. For an account of
the famous saving of the Soviet physicist Landau's life, see A. Dorozynski, *The Man
They Wouldn't Let Die* (New York: The Macmillan Company, 1956).
  For recent popular articles on "bringing back the dead" and treating death as a
reversible process, see "The Reversal of Death," *The Saturday Review*, August 4,
1962; "A New Fight Against Sudden Death," *Look*, December 1, 1964.
  Soviet efforts and conceptions of death as reversible might be seen to have
their ideological basis in principles of dialectics:

> For everyday purposes we know and can say, e.g., whether an animal is
> alive or not. But, upon closer inquiry, we find that this is, in many cases a
> very complex question, as the jurists know very well. They have cudg-
> elled their brains in vain to discover a rational limit beyond which the
> killing of the child in its mother's womb is murder. It is just as impossible
> to determine absolutely the moment of death, for physiology provides
> that death is not an instantaneous, momentary phenomenon, but a very
> protracted process.
> In like manner, every organized being is every moment the same and not
> the same. . . .

From F. Engels, *Socialism: Utopian and Scientific* (New York: International Publishers
Co., Inc., 1935), p. 47.
  For a discussion of primitive conceptions of death with particular attention to
the passage between life and death, see I. A. Lopatin, *The Cult of the Dead Among
the Natives of the Amur Basin* (The Hague: Mouton and Company, 1960), pp. 26–27
and 39–41.

very intensive, such developments would more likely be encouraged than at County).

Currently, at County, there seems to be a rather strong relationship between the age, social backgrounds, and the perceived moral character of patients and the amount of effort that is made to attempt revival when "clinical death signs" are detected (and, for that matter, the amount of effort given to forestalling their appearance in the first place). As one compares practices in this regard at different hospitals, the general relationship seems to hold; although at the private, wealthier institutions, like Cohen, the over-all amount of attention given to "initially dead" patients is greater. At County, efforts at revival are admittedly superficial, with the exception of the very young or occasionally wealthier patient, who by some accident ends up at County's ER. No instances have been witnessed, at County, where, for example, external heart massage was given a patient whose heart was stethoscopically inaudible, if that patient was over 40 years of age. At Cohen Hospital, on the other hand, heart massage is a normal routine at that point, and more drastic measures, such as the injection of adrenalin directly into the heart, are not uncommon. While these practices are undertaken for many patients at Cohen if "tentative death" is discovered early (and it typically is because of the attention "dying" patients are given), at County they are reserved for a very special class of cases.

Generally speaking, the older the patient the more likely is his tentative death taken to constitute pronounceable death. Before a 20-year-old who arrives in the ER with a presumption of death attached in the form of the ambulance driver's assessment will be pronounced dead by a physician, very long listening to his heartbeat will occur, occasionally efforts at stimulation will be made, oxygen administered, and oftentimes stimulative medication given. Less time will elapse between initial detection of an inaudible heartbeat and nonpalpable pulse and the pronouncement of death if the person is 40 years old, and still less if he is 70. As best as can be detected, there appeared to be no obvious difference between men and women in this regard, nor between white and Negro "patients." Very old patients who are initially considered to be dead solely on the basis of the ambulance driver's assessment of that possibility, were seen to be put in an empty room and "wait" several moments before a physician arrived. The driver's announcement of a "possible" places a frame of interpretation around the event, so that the physician expects to find a dead person and attends the person under the general auspices of that expectation. When a young person is brought in as a "possible," the driver tries to convey some more alarming sense to the arrival by turning the siren up very loud and keeping it going after he has already stopped, so that by the time he has actually entered the wing, personnel, expecting "something special," act quickly and accordingly. When it is a younger person that the driver is delivering his general manner is more frantic. The speed with which he wheels his stretcher in, and the degree of excitement in his voice as he describes his charge to the desk clerk, are generally more heightened than with the typical elderly "DOA." One can observe a direct relationship between the loudness and length of the siren alarm and the considered "social value" of the person being transported.[27] The older the person, the less thorough is the examination he is given; frequently, elderly people are pronounced dead on the basis of only a stethoscopic examination of the heart. The younger the person, the more likely will an examination preceding an announcement of death entail an inspection of the eyes, attempt to find a pulse, touching of the body for coldness, etc. When a younger person is brought to the hospital and announced by the driver as a "possible" but is nonetheless observed to be breathing slightly, or have an audible heart beat, there is a fast mobilization of effort to stimulate increased breathing and a more rapid heartbeat. If an older person is brought in in a similar condition there will be a rapid mobilization of similar efforts; however, the time which will elapse between that point at which breathing noticeably ceases and the heart audibly stops beating, and when the pronouncement of death is made, will differ according to his age.

One's location in the age structure of the society is not the only factor that will influence the degree of care he gets when his death is considered possibly to have occurred. At County Hospital a notable additional set of considerations, relating to the patient's presumed "moral character," is made to apply. The detection of alcohol on the breath of a "DOA" is nearly always noticed by the examining physician, who announces to his fellow workers that the person is a drunk. This seems to constitute a feature he regards as warranting less than strenuous effort to attempt revival. The alcoholic patient is treated by hospital physicians, not only when the status of his body as alive or dead is at stake, but throughout the whole course of medical treatment, as one for whom the concern to treat can properly operate somewhat weakly. There is a high proportion of alcoholic patients at County, and their treatment very often involves an earlier admission of "terminality" and a consequently more marked suspension of curative treatment than is observed in the treatment of nonalcoholic patients. In one case, the decision whether or not to administer additional blood needed by an alcoholic man bleeding badly from a stomach ulcer was decided negatively, and that decision was announced as based on the fact of his

[27] For a discussion of "social loss value" in the context of nurses' feelings about the death of patients, see A. Strauss and B. Glaser, "The Social Loss of Dying Patients," *American Journal of Nursing*, 64, No. 6 (June, 1964).

alcoholism. The intern in charge of treating the patient was asked by a nurse, "Should we order more blood for this afternoon?" and the doctor answered, "I can't see any sense in pumping it into him because even if we can stop the bleeding, he'll turn around and start drinking again and next week he'll be back needing more blood." In the DOA circumstance, alcoholic patients have been known to be pronounced dead on the basis of a stethoscopic examination of the heart alone, even though such persons were of such an age that were they not alcoholics they would likely have received much more intensive consideration before being so decided upon. Among other categories of persons whose deaths will be more quickly adjudged, and whose "dying" more readily noticed and used as a rationale for palliative care, are the suicide victim, the dope addict, the known prostitute, the assailant in a crime of violence, the vagrant, the known wife-beater, and, generally, those persons whose moral characters are considered reproachable.

Within a limited temporal perspective at least, but one which is not necessarily to be regarded as trivial, the likelihood of "dying" and even of being "dead" can be said to be partially a function of one's place in the social structure, and not simply in the sense that the wealthier get better care, or at least not in the usual sense of that fact.[28] If one anticipates having a critical heart attack, he had best keep himself well-dressed and his breath clean if there is a likelihood he will be brought into the County Emergency Unit as a "possible."

There are a series of practical consequences of pronouncing a patient dead in the hospital setting. His body may be properly stripped of clothing, jewelry, and the like, wrapped up for discharge, the family notified of the death, the coroner informed in the case of DOA deaths, etc. In the Emergency Unit there is a special set of procedures which can be said to be partially definitive of death. DOA cases are very interestingly "used" in many American hospitals. The inflow of dead bodies, or what can properly be taken to be dead bodies, is regarded as a collection of "guinea pigs," in the sense that a set of procedures can be performed upon those bodies for the sake of teaching and research.

In any "teaching hospital" (in the case of County, I use that term

---

[28] The "DOA" deaths of famous persons are reportedly attended with considerably prolonged and intensive resuscitation efforts. In Kennedy's death, for example, it was reported:

> Medically, it was apparent the President was not alive when he was brought in. There was no spontaneous respiration. He had dilated, fixed pupils. It was obviously a lethal head wound.
> Technically, however, by using vigorous resuscitation, intraveneous tubes and all the usual supportive measures, we were able to raise the semblance of a heart beat.

The New York Times, November 23, 1963, p. 2.

in a weak sense, i.e., a hospital which employs interns and residents;
in other settings a "teaching hospital" may mean systematic, institutionalized instruction), the environment of medical events is regarded not
merely as a collection of treatable cases, but as a collection of experience-
relevant information. It is a continually enforced way of looking at the
cases one treats to regard them under the auspices of a concern for experience with "such cases." That concern can legitimately warrant the
institution of a variety of procedures, tests, inquiries, and the like, which
lie outside and may even, on occasion, conflict with the strict interests of
treatment; they fall within the interests of learning "medicine," gain-
ing experience with such cases, acquiring technical skills, etc. A principle
for organizing medical care activities in the teaching hospital generally,
and perhaps more so in the county hospital, where patients' social value
is often not highly regarded, is the relevance of any particular activity
to the acquisition of skills of general import. Physicians feel about such
institutions that among their greatest values lies the ease with which
warrant can be given to selectively organizing medical attention so as
to maximize the general benefits to knowledge and technical proficiency
which working with a given case expectably afford. The notion of the
"interesting case" is, at County, not simply a casual notion, but an enforced principle for the allocation of attention. The private physician
is in a more committed relation to each and every one of his patients; and
while he may regard this or that case as more or less interesting, he
ideally cannot legitimate the interestingness of his patients' conditions as
a basis for devoting varying amounts of attention to them (his reward
for treating the uninteresting case is, of course, the fee, and physicians are
known to give more attention to those of their patients who shall be
paying more).

At County Hospital, a case's degree of interest is a crucial fact, and
one which is invoked to legitimate the way a physician does and should
allocate his attention. In surgery, for instance, I found many examples.
If, on a given morning in one operating room a "rare" procedure was
scheduled, and in another a "usual" procedure planned, there would be
no special difficulty in getting personnel to witness and partake in the
"rare" procedure, whereas work in the "usual" case was considered as
merely work, regardless of such considerations as the relative fatality
rate of each procedure, the patient's physical condition, and the like. It
is not uncommon to find interns at County interchange among themselves
in scrubbing for an appendectomy, each taking turns going next door to
watch the skin graft or chest surgery.[29] On the medical wards, on the

[29] At Cohen, such house staff interchanging was not permitted. Interns and residents
were assigned to a particular surgical suite and required to stay throughout the
course of the procedure.

basis of general observation it seems that one could obtain a high order correlation between the amount of time doctors spent discussing and examining patients and the degree of unusualness of their medical problems.

I introduce this general feature to point to the predominant orientation, at County, to such matters as "getting practice" and the general organizational principle that provides for the propriety of using cases as the basis for this practice. Not only are live patients objects of practice, so are dead ones. There is a rule, in the Emergency Unit, that with every DOA a doctor should attempt to insert an "endo-trachial" tube down the throat. This should be done only after the patient is pronounced dead. The reason for this practice (and it is a rule on which new interns are instructed as part of their training in doing emergency medicine), is that such a tube is extremely difficult to insert, requiring great yet careful force and, insofar as it may entail great pain, cannot be "practiced" on live patients. The body must be so positioned with the neck held at such an angle that this large tube will go down the proper channel. In some circumstances when it is necessary to establish a rapid "airway" (an open breathing canal), the endo-trachial tube can apparently be an effective substitute for the tracheotomy incision. The DOA's body in its transit from the scene of the death to the morgue constitutes an ideal captive experimental opportunity. The procedure is not done on all deceased patients, the reason apparently being that it is part of the training one receives on the Emergency Unit, and to be learned there. Nor is it done on all DOA cases, for some doctors, it seems, are uncomfortable in handling a dead body whose charge as a live one they never had, and handling it in the way such a procedure requires. It is important to note that when it is done, it is done most frequently and most intensively with those persons who are regarded as lowly situated in the moral social structure.

No instances were observed where a young child was used as an object for such a practice, nor where a well-dressed, middle-aged, middle-class adult was similarly used. On one occasion a woman supposed to have ingested a fatal amount of Clorox was brought to the Emergency Unit, and several physicians, after she died, took turns trying to insert an endo-trachial tube, after which one of them suggested that the stomach be pumped to examine its contents to try to see what effects the clorox had on the gastric secretions. A lavage was set up and the stomach contents removed. A chief resident left the room and gathered together a group of interns with the explanation that they ought to look at this woman because of the apparent results of such ingestion. In effect, the doctors conducted their own autopsy investigation without making any incisions.

On several similar occasions physicians explained that with these
kinds of cases they didn't really feel like they were prying in handling
the body, but that they often did in the case of an ordinary death, i.e., a
"natural death" of a morally proper person. Suicide victims are frequently the object of curiosity, and while there is a high degree of distaste in working with such patients and their bodies (particularly among
the nursing staff; some nurses will not touch a suicide victim's dead
body), "practice" by doctors is apparently not as distasteful. A woman
was brought into the Emergency Unit with a gunshot wound, self-
inflicted, which ran from her sternum downward and backward, passing
out through a kidney. She had apparently bent over a rifle and pulled the
trigger. Upon her "arrival" in the Emergency Unit she was quite alive and
talkative, and while in great pain and very fearful, was able to conduct
something of a conversation. She was told that she would need immediate
surgery and was taken off to the O.R.; following her were a group of
physicians, all of whom were interested in seeing what damage the path
of the bullet had done. (One doctor said aloud, quite near her stretcher, "I
can't get my heart into saving her, so we might as well have some fun
out of it.") During the operation, the doctors regarded her body much as
they do one during an autopsy. After the critical damage was repaired
and they had reason to feel the woman would survive, they engaged in
numerous surgical side ventures, exploring muscular tissue in areas of the
back through which the bullet had passed but where no damage requiring special repair had to be done, with the exception of tying off bleeders
and suturing. One of the operating surgeons performed a side operation,
incising an area of skin surrounding the entry wound on the chest, to
examine, he announced to colleagues, the structure of the tissue through
which the bullet passed. He explicitly announced his project to be motivated by curiosity; one of the physicians spoke of the procedure as an
"autopsy on a live patient," about which there was a little laughter.

In another case, a man was wounded in the forehead by a bullet, and
after the damage was repaired in the wound, which resembled a natural
frontal lobotomy, an exploration was made of an area adjacent to the path
of the bullet, on the forehead proper, below the hair line. During this
exploration the operating surgeon asked a nurse to ask Dr. X to come in,
and when Dr. X arrived, the two of them, under the gaze of a large group
of interns and nurses, made a further incision, which an intern described
to me as unnecessary in the treatment of the man, and which left a noticeable scar down the side of the temple. The purpose of this venture was
to explore the structure of that part of the face.[30] The doctors justified

---

[30] This area of the skull, that below the hair line, cannot be examined during an
autopsy because of a contract between local morticians and the Department of
Pathology, designed to leave those areas of the body which will be viewed free of
surgical incisions.

the additional incision by pointing to the "fact" that since he would have a "nice scar as it was, a little bit more wouldn't be so serious."

During autopsies themselves, bodies are routinely used to gain experience in surgical techniques, and many incisions, explorations, and the like are conducted that are not essential to the key task of uncovering the "cause" of the death. On frequent occasions, specialists-in-training come to autopsies having no interest in the patient's death, and they await the completion of the legal part of the procedure, at which point the body is turned over to them for practice. Mock surgical procedures are staged on the body, oftentimes with co-workers simulating actual conditions, tying off blood vessels which obviously need not be tied, suturing internally, and the like.

❦❦❦ LIFE AND DEATH: A Special Case of Interdependence

To this point I have examined some of the practices at the hospital surrounding "dying" and "death" and have sought to reiterate the point that these categories of events are employed in various ways in different settings within the hospital, are embedded in the context of ongoing organizational activities and views of the patient population, and are thus always capable of being at least partially regarded as social categories. The final section of this chapter shall be devoted to the discussion of a rather special setting of "death" and "dying"—the circumstance of the stillborn and premature "death."[31]

At County Hospital, there is a system of definitions and weights intended to describe the status of fetuses. According to its weight, length, and period of gestation at the end of which it is delivered (or, "expelled"), a fetus is either considered "human" or not. At County, the dividing line is 550 grams, 20 centimeters, and 20 weeks of gestation. Any creature having smaller dimensions or of lesser embryonic "age" is considered non-human (or better, is not considered "human"; a term sometimes used to describe such a "thing" is an "aborted fetus," or, simply, "abortus"), and if "born" without signs of life, is flushed down the toilet or otherwise simply disposed of, placed in a jar for pathological examination, or the like. Any creature having larger dimensions or greater embryonic "age" is considered human, and if "born" without signs of life, or if born with signs of life which cease to be noticeable at some later point, cannot permissibly be flushed down the toilet, but must be accorded a proper ritual departure from the human race. Not only must it be properly departed, it must, as a condition for being departed, be first admitted. We are dealing here with a "thing" which, at the minimum level of acceptability, would be

[31] For general discussion of the definitional problems in this area, see G. Williams, *op. cit.*, pp. 5–10.

about the size and weight of a pound of butter. This "human" must be admitted to the hospital, wrapped in a morgue sheet, placed in the hospital morgue, and buried in the ground by an authorized burier. Creatures under the definitional limit are not considered to be "dead," for to be "dead," where being "dead" consists of that status which requires a variety of Death Procedures, one must first be capable of being seen as something which at least could have been alive, and "life," in turn, is not simply the biological phenomenon of cellular activity, or some such thing, but is a socially constituted state of affairs. A "thing" which makes the limit will have its existence duly recorded in the official tallies of the society, from the hospital's yearly demographic inventory to the U.S. Census Reports.

A fetus of 15 weeks' gestation, weighing less than one pound and shorter than six inches, which pulsates, for example, is nonetheless not a live human, for a live human is procedurally defined, in the hospital, as a creature which, for example, is to be admitted to the hospital and can die, i.e., be treated as a dead person, given a burial, etc. A pulsating non-human will not be disposed of, nor will it be admitted to the hospital; its status will be that simply of a "thing," and once it stops pulsating, which almost universally occurs after its expulsion from the womb and detachment from the placenta, it will be disposed of. It does not move from life to death, as these categories are socially used, but from biological activity to inactivity. No attempts will be made to keep it pulsating, despite the fact that some doctors agree that biological activity can be artificially stimulated and thereby sustained for an extended period of time. A pediatrician explained that a fetus of some 18 or 20 weeks' gestation could be kept alive for some time if placed in an incubator and fed artificially. He noted that this has been achieved on an experimental basis. Whether feasible or possible, or not, so far as I could tell such efforts were not made; these "things" are considered nonviable.

The fetus that passes the definitional limit and is considered a "human," dead or alive, is, however, not always treated as the regulations require. The 20-week-gestated fetus, exceeding 20 centimeters and 550 grams, is, if pulsating at birth, ideally to be placed in an incubator and treated as a hospital patient. In over 95 per cent of the cases a fetus of that size will not survive more than a few hours or days after birth, even when incubated, given the current state of medical skill in these areas (and perhaps, in turn, the medical concern to develop them). The survival rate currently increases in a clear straight linear progression with increased weight and gestation (and that relationship may be partially a function of the kind of care given fetuses of different sizes). If the fetus is a borderline case, staff members will not, generally, put it in an incubator, but rather, by keeping it in open air, allow it to "die" very shortly after its delivery. Should the fetus cry, however, or take what is regarded as a breath, it will be incubated, the cry or sound seemingly taken to represent a more developed embryo—once sounds are uttered, regarding its status as a "thing" seems to be hard to do. At Cohen Hospital, a similar practice exists. If the "baby" takes a breath or cries, that fact is taken to constitute evidence of its humanness and warrants regarding its possible life or possible death as the lives and deaths of other humans are normally regarded.[32] A difference at Cohen is that burials are not required unless the family requests them, even for a full-term stillborn child, while at County proper burials are required for a definitionally adequate "human" that is recorded as such. The fact of "crying" or "breathing" is of social significance, it seems, because, as best as can be gathered from discussions I had with medical personnel, these occurrences in themselves have no special medical significance. The 20-week-gestated fetus that cries is in no better shape, medically speaking, than a similarly aged one that is "silent" ("silent" is perhaps not an appropriate term, for to be "silent" one must presumably be capable of "silencing"). The facts of "crying" or "breathing" seem to be socially significant, as "cries for help" as it were.

Delivery room staff have some latitude in assigning the statuses of life, death, human, or "abortus," for such determinations are not always precisely made with the use of a scale. The decision in any given case rests upon whether medical and nursing personnel assess the "thing's" life chances as good or poor, and upon what they assess as the consequences of assigning status for other activities, which shall be discussed below. While weight and length and "age" are generally employed as rough guides, the exhibition of "human behavior" in the form of a cry or breath can operate to provide the "thing" which is legally under the limit with the status of a "human" and the absence of such "behavior" is often taken to legitimate treating an otherwise legal "human" as an "abortus," particularly if its dimensions barely exceed borderline requirements.

While some flexibility is permissible in assigning these statuses, there is always care exercised in attempting to treat that which might be properly considered as a "human" by disposal. This care is warranted by the fact that certain patients are known to be overly sensitive about such "products" of theirs and to complain that what they regarded as "their baby" was treated as a specimen. Catholic patients are regarded as especially troublesome in this respect, and Catholic staff members are characteristically more conservative in their use of the definitional criteria (some of the Catholic staff members claim that they are too high). On several known occasions Catholic "parents" issued complaints when they learned that "their babies" were disposed of, and in various instances at County a Catholic intern or resident required a duly recorded entry and dismissal of a "thing" which other delivery room staff would have preferred to treat as a specimen. There is the general feeling among the

[32] G. Williams, *op. cit.*, p. 7., has a discussion of the significance of "breathing."

Protestant members of the delivery room staff that the legal definitions
are too strict and too low, and that the procedures of wrapping, discharging, and burying a one-pound fetus border on obscenity. Once a death
certificate is made out, the procedures of discharge, wrapping, and burial
must be carried out, and the doctor has the final decision in whether or
not to prepare such a certificate. One Catholic intern got a relatively bad
name for himself in the delivery room by preparing such certificates for
almost all deliveries of nonviable creatures, and despite attempts to "reason with him," taken by other interns, residents, and nurses, he insisted
upon his right to make such decisions.

The circumstances of a delivery are especially interesting from the
standpoint of the relative's awareness of the death, for here, unlike other
circumstances at County, the relative is immediately present at the scene
of "death," and this scene is known to generate rather tense moments.
Women in our society (and perhaps everywhere) expect their newly delivered infants to cry aloud rather shortly after delivery, and indeed they
normally do. The longer the amount of time between the complete expulsion of the infant from the womb and the point when crying begins, the
more tense the interactional situation becomes. The practice at County is
immediately to put the "mother" to sleep when a biologically troublesome
infant is delivered. Modern gas anesthetics allow for a very rapid induc-
tion of sleep so that at that point when physicians feel crying will never
come, or feel that the time passage has obviously gotten too extended,
they give a well understood visual order to the attending nurse or anes-
thetist to administer gas. Women are often kept considerably doped up
during the final moments of their deliveries, and one obstetrician reported
that this is done as much so as to be able quickly to put them under if
trouble occurs as for their pain during the delivery. Obstetricians employ
an interesting device to handle the perpetually possible situation of
trouble: as soon as the baby's head appears at the opening of the vagina,
they obtain a suctioning syringe. When the head itself comes out sufficiently far so that the mouth can be entered, the doctor starts to suction
mucus and stimulate crying. The reason for this practice, over and above
the general concern to get the infant quickly on "outside air," is that the
sooner the doctor attempts to stimulate crying the sooner he will be able
to detect trouble and have time to order anesthesia before the mother becomes aware of any difficulty. Mothers expect to hear crying once they
have delivered the entire baby, which they can apparently feel; starting
suctioning early thus gives the doctor a safety margin as regards the simultaneous detection of trouble. The arrangement whereby the mother
cannot witness from her position what goes on "down-under," aids in
giving the doctor leeway (obstetricians complained, at County, about the
new practice whereby a mirror is placed in such a way that women can

witness the delivery of the child; this mirror allows the mother more scrutiny over the critical area and its happenings than some doctors, at least, prefer for them to have).

Should the mother detect trouble, however (which seems to occur infrequently), she is vaguely and evasively told not to worry, and gas is quickly given, usually with an explanation to the mother that gas must be given before suturing the episiotomy occurs. In several known instances mothers were observed to cry out such things as "My baby is dead, isn't it?" Doctors at County do not treat this as a question, but instead respond with something like, "Relax, Mrs.—" (or at County, often, "Miss") and gas is quickly administered.

The most frequent occasion of the delivery of a "dead" fetus is the premature delivery, and the more premature the delivery is, the more the "mother" expects a nonviable being to be expelled. It is with the unexpected stillborn delivery that interactional problems are most severe, though even here, very few instances at County were observed where anesthetics were insufficient to manage at least temporarily the task of separating the relative from the scene of the "death."

Doctors and nurses use, as indications of the mother's attachment to the "child-to-be," the manner of her behavior throughout the course of her delivery and in those critical moments of silence. At County, there is the general feeling that a great proportion of the newborns are "unwanted," and this is said to be substantiated by the fact that premature deliveries and deliveries of stillborns are not only taken coolly, but are often occasions for the expression of relief. On three known occasions, women were heard to express joy with the delivery of a nonviable "infant." The more indifferent the mother's attitude toward the process of childbirth and in that period of tense silence which attends the delivery of a "baby-in-trouble," the more comfortable staff members feel about treating a borderline case as nonhuman. The woman who, throughout the course of her delivery, moans that she doesn't want the baby, is regarded as one who will be least upset if a barely adequate "legal human" is later treated as a specimen.

In the greatest proportion of cases, despite the slight degree of latitude delivery room personnel have in making such decisions, the outcome of distributions into the various status categories corresponds closely to the weight, length, and age criteria. The consequences of treating a one-pound, six-inch, "thing," as a "human" are worthy of some comment, for a special set of administrative problems surrounds the handling of these "things," having to do with the responsibility of having a burial, and with the social organization of the hospital morgue.

These special consequences of "death" provide that category with some additional interesting social features. Such "things" are wrapped up and placed in the hospital morgue, and the "parents" are informed that it is their responsibility to contact a funeral parlor to arrange for a burial for their "child." A very common happening at County, one which staff members characteristically point to as prototypical of the general "immorality" of the patient population, is that such "babies" are very frequently deserted in the morgue, i.e., no funeral parlor is contacted and, after a period of days, weeks, and in some cases months, the "baby's" remains remain in the morgue. Many such "parents" are hard to reach, for, it is maintained, many of them give incorrect names on their admission to the hospital, particularly the unmarried "mothers."

The county has a service which it provides for the relatives of those families who cannot afford a funeral service and who can provide evidence of this financial inability—a county burial. The hospital employs a "funeral director," has a very old hearse which it uses to transport deceased patients from the hospital to the county cemetery, and, in the basement of the hospital, devotes a large section of the carpentry department to the manufacture of caskets, a practice which seems nonexistent in noncharity hospitals in the United States. If the relatives desire, and make adequate arrangements in advance, a simple graveside ceremony can be conducted. Very few of County's deceased patients' families are able to demonstrate their eligibility for this service, because the hospital maintains a list of private funeral establishments that offer reduced rates for charity patients, and these rates are sometimes very low. The hospital "eligibility workers" in charge of screening families in this respect have a rule that if any private establishment's services can be afforded, as they assess what persons can afford, the county burial will be refused. An eligibility worker reported that in fact there are few requests made for such services, that most families want to give their deceased relatives private funerals, and that many of the families have funeral insurance and family plots. The same is not true as regards stillborns and "premies."

The same requirement for demonstrating financial inability operates to obtain a county burial for a "deceased stillborn," or "deceased premie." The "parents" must come to the hospital, with an appointment to "see an eligibility worker" (the phrasing of the admitting nurses who often spends half her day telephoning families to inform them of this "responsibility"), and arrange to have the county bury their "child." It is interesting that the terms "child" and "baby" are used to refer to these objects, while those below the limit are never so referred to. The admitting nurse uses, as one device to get families to come in for interviews, a form letter which she sends three times, after which the police are notified of the case. The letter begins:

Dear _____,
This letter is regarding the burial of your baby, born _____.

A major hospital effort is required to keep the morgue relatively free of a large backlog of piled up, wrapped "fetuses." At any given time in the morgue there are usually some 20 such packages, as compared with the usual morgue census of half a dozen adult bodies, yet the death rate is higher among adults. On repeated occasions the number became so excessive that morgue personnel became rather desperate, in part because of the terrible stench that was created which the pathologist claimed kept doctors from attending autopsies, and in part because needed space was taken up by these "things." When such a situation occurred, pressure was exerted upon the eligibility staff to authorize county burials, despite the lack of formal interviews with families. The concern to keep the turn-over rate high occasionally operated to legitimate a more lenient attitude toward financial responsibility, so that if a "parent" simply came into the hospital and said he could not afford a private burial, the OK was given. Periodically, a vigorous campaign to dispose of the backlog was instituted, and the admitting nurse spent several days on the telephone trying to contact as many "parents" as was possible. Once a rule was established that if a "baby" stayed in the morgue for more than six weeks, it could be buried without a financial interview, and once a large batch of "babies" was thereby carried out. Usually, the casket makers in the basement prepare special little boxes for these burials, but on this occasion, much to the later dismay of the hospital administrator, all were placed in a single adult coffin, whereupon the six-week rule was abolished.

The entire situation of the "premie death" is regarded by many people at County as rather obnoxious. The requirement for a burial, uncommon at other hospitals where that matter is up to the family to decide, is thought to result from the Catholic District Attorney's peculiar interest and special personal influence in such matters. "Death" and "dying" become particularly interesting in this area, where a "thing," by virtue of a system of numerical definitions, can become the discussed, responsible object of a variety of administrative officials and a cumbersome bureaucratic set of procedures established by virtue of a difference in ounces of flesh. If a fetus makes a cry or takes a breath it thereby establishes its right to treatment within some of the ordinary economic, administrative, ritual, and familial institutions of the welfare and civil society. Its social existence can be established if it grows, prenatally, to an adequate size. Form letters speaking of it as a "baby," the manufacture of miniature caskets, the requirement for fulfilling "parental" responsibilities toward it, its entry into the official demographic records via the required birth and death certificates—these are among the treatments which make such an object a social one; they can be said to constitute a minimal definition of life and death. There is a beginning, and an end, and nothing much in between but perhaps a heartbeat or two, yet that beginning and end are marked by the standardized, obligatory, societal forms by which all beginnings and ends are attended.

Perhaps one of the reasons County has such difficulty in having "parents" assume their "responsibilities" toward their dead offspring is that the notion of a "parent" is not mutually shared by eligibility staff and these men and women, and not that these people are "irresponsible." The enforcement of a responsibility to bury one's kin would seem to operate only if the respect for the deceased person as a "kin" is operative. In the delivery room, women are often addressed as "mother," even though they may have no children, and oftentimes before the infants they are expected to deliver are actually delivered. Obstetricians at County (and Cohen as well) characteristically conversed with their patients before and during the delivery, and used the term "mother" in directing comments to them, giving advice, instructions, asking for their sensations, etc. This usage is not employed, generally, until the woman actually comes into the delivery room and begins to "crown," i.e., when the baby's head appears at the opening of the vagina, though the head had not actually begun to pass through itself. That appearance is taken to warrant such talk as "Come on now, mother, you're doing fine, take a deep breath," or "A little while more, mother, and it will be here," or "His head is coming through, mother, one more good push and it will be all over." A woman who is five months pregnant and therefore considered about to deliver a nonviable "thing," will not be so referred to in the delivery room, even if she is a mother, in fact, by virtue of the children she has at home. The use of the term "mother" is rather special here, referring as it does not to a formally constituted kinship category, but to "mothering," conceived as the activity of producing what is likely to be a live, human child. Caution is used in employing the term the shorter the length of the woman's pregnancy, typically being restricted only to those women who are at full term. Should a woman at full term be referred to as "mother" and then deliver a stillborn infant, all further references to her as "mother" are thereupon suspended.

It is a matter outside the scope of the present chapter to consider the special properties of "motherhood" under varying conditions, e.g., when an older child dies and is an only child, do "parents" retain their claims to be so referred to? Can a woman properly consider herself a "mother" even though she has no other children other than the one who was born a stillborn? In the County case, given the use of "mother" in this special, prebirth, perhaps preparatory way, we can have the circumstance of a woman being a "mother," in the sense of being entitled to be so referred to, even though she has never had children, and was properly so called only during that period of time between the beginning of her delivery and the birth of a stillborn. Yet at the same time, she is expected to oblige by "family responsibilities" in arranging a funeral for "her child."

FIVE

On Bad News

♚ ♚ ♚ THERE IS A CLASS of hospital-situated events of such status that it is considered mandatory that their occurrence be reported to members of a patient's family, whether or not inquiry is made about them. A "sudden turn for the worse," the outcome of a surgical procedure, the result of a child delivery, the findings of a laboratory investigation of expected import, and the occurrence of a death, are among member events of this class. I shall term such events "announceable events."[1]

It is a property of this class of events that associated with it is a rule regarding those personnel who are to be responsible for reporting its events and those who are specifically prohibited from doing so. At County, the distribution of personnel with respect to this responsibility is physicians—others; at Cohen, the distribution is physician-in-charge-of-the-case —others. Should inquiry be made concerning an announceable event to a member of the staff with no authority to announce such events, the inquirer is referred to a proper person, i.e., should a relative at County inquire of a nurse: "What did the test show?" he is to be referred to *a* physician; should a relative ask a Cohen nurse the same question, he must be referred to the patient's private physician. Stating this rule differently, hospital staff can be seen to be divided into announcers and nonannouncers.

Expectations regarding announceable events are mutually held, so

---

[1] By such a listing I do not intend to suggest that there is not a much wider variety of matters which one feels obliged to report upon, so that, for example, the nurse will feel responsible for relaying a message from a patient to a member of his family. I intend to restrict attention to those events which have a clearly perceived announcement-type structure, events with presentational formats such as, "I have something to tell you."

that members of the public take it that they will be informed about the occurrence of such events without having to undertake inquiries, i.e., no discovery procedure need be engaged in to learn how the surgery went, what the lab result was, what the sex and condition of the newborn is, whether or not his relative is still alive. While such inquiries are oftentimes made, the inquirer takes it that they need not be made, but that he will be informed. So, for example, the question "How did it go?" need not be asked to obtain information about such events; rather, such a question, when asked in such circumstances appears to be an opening conversational device. When inquiries are made, those with no authority to announce such events feel obliged, it seems, to inform the inquirer that he will be informed by the proper person, i.e., the inquirer is told of the rule regarding announcing authority. It is to be noted that the class "announceable events" is generally used in the society; members hold expectations regarding those matters which they feel entitled to be told of. It is also to be noted, and my later discussion will treat the issue, that events which are announceable to some are not felt to require announcement to others, i.e., there is, with respect to any given announceable event, a rule of entitlement specifying those to whom an announcement is due and those to whom it is not.

With respect to most announceable events in the hospital, specifically structured episode occasions are found. Persons await the outcome of a surgical procedure, of laboratory investigations known to be in progress, expectant fathers the births of their children. Awaiting news of these events occurs within clearly framed outcome situations, with a well defined expectation on the part of awaiting members. It is a key organizational fact about deaths, however, that they do not usually occur as the outcomes of specifically structured, episodic situations, but rather "take place" in the course of downwardly progressing illnesses. An exception of sorts is the DOA case, where relatives are called to the hospital, typically with little information as to what has transpired, and arrive very much attuned to the scene as a news producing one.[2] Here, however, what alternatives are expected may be very much an unclear matter.

Very seldom does it occur that the circumstances surrounding a hospital death are such that members of a patient's family are in a temporal situation where they await the news of the patient's progress with respect to life and death with anywhere near the degree of tight time-binding with which such matters as surgical outcomes are structured. In episodically structured situations, e.g., the surgery situation,

[2] A classic fictional account of a situation where news of a possible death was awaited in an episodically structured framework is in James Agee's, *A Death in the Family* (New York: McDowell, Obolensky, 1957), Part II.

the delivery room circumstance, and the like, a special degree of forth-rightness is required in the manner of an announcer. If the recipient can regard the appearance of an announcer on the scene as motivated by the news he now brings, then a "right to know" is immediately enforce-able, with the degree of urgency and solemnity apparently commensurate with the presumed severity of the matter about to be announced. In an-nouncing the outcomes of such procedures, announcers feel obliged to avoid circuitous routes to the news. It would be felt highly improper, for example, for the physician announcing the sex and condition of a newborn to an awaiting father to do so by first initiating a conversa-tion and, over the course of that conversation, gradually releasing the waited for information. While many matters which *A* knows about *B* are expectably told in line with considerations of tact, embarrassment, the emotional readiness of the recipient, whether or not it is the place of the one who has the information to tell the other, and the like, in situations of clear expectability that news is forthcoming, such con-siderations are more difficult to sustain. It is no warrant for withholding news of an operation's outcome that it might displease the recipient, for the delay of news of the newborn that the parent had hoped for the opposite sex, etc.[3] Nor can an announcer, in situations where there has been a clearly structured anticipation of news, properly delay giving news. The obligation directly to report such matters, once face-to-face contact is initiated, is at least partially due to the fact that the announce-ment is considered to be of some import and that the recipient is taken to be highly keyed up to hearing some news.

Should staff members wish, for whatever reasons, to avoid telling the waiting relative some news in such circumstances, their main strategy is to avoid contact with him. The more such occasions are structured as episodes, with clear beginnings and ends, the more difficult it is for an announcer to appear before relatives without news. Surgeons, for example, carefully arrange their rounds in the hospital so that once they go into surgery, they will emerge from behind the scrutinized doors only when they carry the news being awaited. Once the surgeon has been behind the doors for some time, he must stay back there until ready for his final emergence. Only in the first few minutes or so does the surgeon have a degree of freedom such that should he reappear within that time, the assumption is that things "haven't yet begun."

In such clear episode-like situations, persons with no authority to relate news both create and rely upon the fiction that the critical event's

[3] There is a key exception that occurs when such news is purposefully withheld from someone because it is presumed likely to be detrimental to his health. In County Hospital, at least, the decision as to whether or not to withhold news was not felt to be the physician's. Doctors would only avoid relating news if they were advised to do so by other members of the family.

occurrence almost coincides with the appearance of the proper announcer, that until he appears there is nothing to relate. Typically there is, in these situations, a clear frontstage-backstage boundary, and persons with no authority to announce can emerge from backstage areas and nonetheless act vis-à-vis the recipient-to-be as though the event whose reporting they await has not yet taken place. While staff members who walked back and forth across the public waiting room as they entered and left the surgical area at Cohen often found that eyes jumped to them every time they appeared, they felt they could rely on the knowledge waiters had of the authority structure.

When the proper announcer appears, his manner is generally such as to convey that now that he is there, there is something to report, while in fact that which is of significance may have occurred some time prior to his appearance. In such situations, staff members rely on the fact that certain procedures have unclearly perceived lengths, so that a recipient can be made to feel that "things are still going on" long after the main work has been completed. In the maternity ward, there is considerable traffic in and out of the doors leading back to the delivery room suites, and in the course of that hour or more between the point when the newborn's sex and health are ascertained and the time when the obstetrician will complete stitching the episiotomy, dress, and have a coffee break before emerging from these doors with the news, a large number of staff members will pass the "father's room," having the news the father awaits, yet without informing him. The same possibility exists in the surgical setting, where persons use the ecology to create the impression that the operation's outcome is not known until just moments before the surgeon himself appears.

Waiters for news furthermore do not have accurate knowledge of the goings on in backstage areas, not knowing, for example, whether or not a particular person appearing from behind the doors was involved in their relative's case. So long as a variety of activities are taken to go on behind the doors, particular personnel cannot be matched with particular cases, unless waiters have personal knowledge of those persons attending their relatives. The backstage area is attended as consisting of a complex maze of independent subareas.

In such situations, where news of import is expected, one can observe announcers to very rapidly give signs as to what recipients are to expect. Should the surgery's outcome be poor, surgeons, as they appear from behind the doors to the operating suites, often assume a decidedly solemn appearance, giving indication to awaiting relatives that the news they bring is unfavorable. Such preparation seeks effectively to place recipients in a subdued frame of mind, so that they don't, for example, rush up to the surgeon with anxious questions, making it more difficult for him to deliver the bad news, but, in anticipation of it, remain silently poised to hear the worst. In instances where news is favorable, announcers are known quickly to indicate that fact in their approach to recipients: they walk very rapidly towards them, attempting to shorten the amount of time when the recipient will be unduly worried. Surgeons have been observed to leave the operating room with broad smiles on their faces, and begin talking long before they get within usual conversational distance. One obstetrician at Cohen characteristically shouted out to relatives the sex of the child as he came nearly running down the hall to them. It seems that a direct relationship exists between the distance at which talk begins and the character of the news. In circumstances of bad news, announcers approach recipients slowly and seldom begin talk before a rather close physical distance separates them, a partial concern being to be in a position where the recipient's response can be shielded from potential onlookers. When good news is brought, everyone present may become involved, the announcement made in tones for all to hear. The most notable setting for this jubilance was the maternity ward, where there was often something of a collective participation in the news by all persons present.[4] At Cohen there seems to be a greater degree of concern for a proper definition of such announcement situations than at County. In the latter setting, where staff view the occasion of a birth as of oftentimes ambivalent meaning for its lower-class clientele (among whom the rate of illegitimate births is very high), the announcements of such events are not so joyously put, and while serious news is not lightly treated at County, one doesn't find there that degree of concern for delicately shielding saddened recipients that is so apparent in the behavior of the Cohen private physicians with members of patients' families.

Physicians use the ecology and perceived expected lengths of procedures in a variety of ways. In the surgical setting, surgeons were observed to finish the critical parts of an operation, turn the sewing-up tasks over to residents and interns, and then take an extended break before having to greet relatives. In one instance, a surgeon was observed to remove his cap, mask, and cloth shoecovers as he adjourned from the operating room proper to the doctor's lounge and then, after chatting for a half hour with his colleagues, put his cap and mask back on, with the mask hanging around his neck in that position which suggests it was just

[4] The occasion of a birth is one of a set of "happy occurrences" where the unacquainted may properly engage one another in talk. Having received such news places a recipient in a position where he may receive congratulatory gestures from mere bystanders, and may feel obliged to give thanks for them. For a discussion of the rules governing the kind of encounter between strangers which a special occasion momentarily transforms into something of a gathering, see E. Goffman, *Behavior in Public Places* (New York: Free Press of Glencoe, Inc., 1963), pp. 125–139.

taken off. He then left the area and talked with the family. With the cap and mask on, he reported afterwards, it appears as though he has just put down the needle and suturing thread and carries exceedingly fresh news.[5]

In situations of a clearly anticipated outcome structure, staff members rely upon the temporal structure of the occasion and its definition as a tense one to provide for that degree of anxiousness on the part of awaiting relatives necessary to minimize the likelihood that they will behave with an inappropriate degree of nonconcern in face of possible bad news. In the case of deaths, which seldom occur within such time-specific, either-or contexts, unless staff effort is quickly taken in the handling of an uniformed relative, there is the likelihood that sufficient self-control will not be exercised but that the unknowlegeable bereaved person will act as though nothing of special import has happened. Those members of the staff who are not permitted to make announcements find themselves in the uncomfortable psychological situation of witnessing a person whom they know is now a bereaved but who is not himself aware of his new status, nor especially attending its possibility. In such a situation, staff members rapidly seek to establish a frame of seriousness, provide the unknowledgeable relative with the sense that something of moment is about to occur for him, and then seek to guarantee the rapid arrival of a proper announcer. What they seek to do is to transform the relative's definition of the situation from one which is "just like another hospital visit" to a perception of the specifically great import of the present moment.

The requirements for a redefinition of the situation most acutely occur should the relative engage the staff members in casual conversation, which is more likely the more extended the patient's stay had been and the more acquainted the relative is with members of the staff. Nurses experience considerable strain when a relative with whom they are well acquainted greets them in the hall in cheerful tones, employing previously useable forms of conversation, facial and body composure, etc., taking it that the conditions which previously and typically warranted their use continue to stand, making their current display appropriate. The fact that those conditions have been altered by an event the occurrence of which is not known to the bereaved-to-be, nor anticipated, places a somewhat deceitful cast on the propriety of allowing interaction to proceed with him "as usual." In undertaking interaction with him, one allows the uninformed bereaved-to-be to enter an encounter assuming that there is a

---

[5] There is apparently always some danger that with such delays the physician will forget about his task. At County, an intern spent a long time talking with a student nurse after he had delivered a baby, and when he left the delivery area to return to his sleeping room, he nearly forgot the relative, almost passing him in the hall before he realized his obligation.

continuity in his own life circumstances such that the present occasion stands, with respect to those which have preceded it, as "another one of them"; that the facts of their relationship, knowledge about each other, remain essentially the same for the present encounter as for those in the past. Personnel not permitted to make announcements have difficulty in such situations, taking it that the bereaved has an immediate right to learn of his bereavement, or, at least, the right to know that a serious matter has occurred, of which he will shortly be informed. The attempt is made to place a new frame around events, to rapidly give the situation an outcome structure, make it an episode, and quickly cut off whatever interaction might develop which would inadvertently be based on the bereaved's ignorance of his own circumstance. Nurses have been observed rapidly to approach an unknowledgeable bereaved-to-be as they see him appear within sight, so as to shorten the period of time when the bereaved would be naively entering a situation which, were he aware of its character, would be approached with cautiousness and preparedness.[6]

While a central basis for the obligation to report an outcome in episodically structured occasions is the very definition of the situation as one wherein an outcome is expected, when a death occurs, whether or not a frame of anticipation has been successfully established, the basis for an obligation to report seems significantly different. I am not suggesting that were there no anticipation of news, the obstetrician, for example, would not feel obliged, nonetheless, to inform a father of a birth, but he would have available to him, without a clearly structured expectation of forthcoming news, a rather great degree of latitude in the manner in which he put his announcement. The immediacy and forthrightness with which such matters as surgical outcomes are announced, once face-to-face contact is made, is largely a function of the definition of the situation and the interactional strain which forestallment would entail. When a piece of announceable information is generated outside of such temporally structured episodes the announcer can employ a variety of considerations, otherwise not allowable, in releasing the news. When surgical procedures are conducted without schedule, as occasionally happens in emergency situations, members of the family might be unaware that an operation has been performed and the surgeon, when reporting

[6] This practice seems generally related to the difficulty persons have in greeting one another from a distance, e.g., when walking toward each other from opposite directions on a sidewalk, when meeting someone at an airplane, etc. Persons seem unable to maintain continuous eye contact in such approach situations without experiencing some uneasiness, and there is usually the sense of incompleteness, wherein an initial greeting is suspended until persons get close enough to follow through the greeting with a more complete sequence. In situations of bad news, the deliverer seeks to shorten this distance rapidly, so as to get close enough for his eyes to convey the seriousness of what is to follow and hence the need to inhibit any typical sociable greeting extension before it gets under way.

its occurrence and results to them, can employ considerations of tact, proper timing, and the like. When a child is unexpectedly delivered, as occasionally happens, obstetricians have been heard to telephone the father and break the news in the context of a joke, as in the following tape-recorded example:

Doctor: . . . Say, this is Dr. M. at Cohen. Are you Mr. X.?

Husband: Yes I am.

Doctor: Well I have something to tell you. It seems your wife came in here this afternoon and complained of a tummy ache and it seems that there was this baby—congratulations Mr. X. You have a nice new little boy.

So long as there is not a clearly established situation of "awaiting the news," physicians and other staff members can delay releasing it. On one occasion, at County, a physician discovered that a patient had a cancerous growth after a lymph-node biopsy was conducted, which the wife of the patient did not know was being done. Rather than tell her immediately, the intern handling the case decided to wait until he had more time to talk with her. He passed her in the hall in the morning, exchanged a casual greeting, and only told her of the cancer later in the afternoon. In a Cohen instance, a surgeon waited for three days before announcing the outcome of a biopsy to a relative who did not know the procedure was performed; the first lab test was not conclusive and he wanted to take a better specimen before considering the results final.[7]

When a death occurs, direct announcement, with no circuity or delay, is enforceable without respect for whether or not the family anticipates its likelihood. The enforceable character of a prompt, straightforward announcement of death derives less from the structure of an occasion than from the strongly held sentiment that persons have a right to be told immediately of their own status as newly bereaved. A laboratory test that indicates the presence of an incurable disease will be felt to be an announceable matter. Unless, however, the family is expected to be awaiting such an announcement and they view a physician's particular encounter with them as generated by the news of the outcome, the physician may release such news with considerably less urgency, framing it so as sensitively to attend the relative's fears, expectations, and the like. When a death occurs, staff members feel the unknowledgeable bereaved has a right to an urgent telling; and with every moment that

---

[7] The more there exists a situation of close doctor-relative communication, the less likely are announceable events to get generated outside of predefined situations of anticipation. At Cohen Hospital, nearly every matter of import occurring in the course of a patient's stay in the hospital was set within an episode. Seldom was there a significant lab test made that wasn't announced to the family in advance as planned. At County, on the other hand, many biopsies, and even surgical procedures were conducted without the family knowing beforehand.

passes in which the unknowledgeable bereaved remains ignorant, no matter how effectively the situation has been given episodic features and the relative is made aware that something of great moment has occurred, staff feel more uneasy in having him around. Nurses, not properly able to announce deaths, have been observed to leave the scene of such an awaiting bereaved-to-be because they could not retain their own composure. This was the case most noticeably on the pediatrics ward, when a young child had died, and, generally, seemed most acutely bothersome where, for whatever reasons, staff members found themselves saddened by the death and sympathetic toward the bereaved.

A set of resources generally available in nondeath circumstances are not useable here. Personnel cannot advise the family not to worry, nor do they feel up to engaging in niceties, exchanging smiles, or otherwise doing those things which they might to help the recipient fill the time until the proper announcer arrives. In the surgery situation, nurses in the station adjacent to the waiting room had the task of acting as objects of tension reduction by conducting passing talk with anxious waiters. When a death occurred, however, staff members felt that to say anything whatever was unkind, as it risked invitation to discourse which, they felt, the bereaved-to-be would not wish to engage in were he to know the details of his circumstances. While in the episodically structured situation the fiction that no news exists prior to the doctor's appearance allows staff to make conversation, when they know of a death's occurrence a qualitatively different attitude in their regard for a recipient-to-be prevails. The whole class of comforting remarks and gestures, otherwise appropriate, are, with death, considered radically inappropriate. Until death, staff members have available, as devices for offering comfort, the use of qualifications on the actual seriousness of the occurrence. For cancers, it is proposed that there is always the hope of X-ray therapy, and further surgery, for "sudden turns for the worse" always the chance that he will "pull through." Every announcement in the hospital, save that of a death, can properly have appended to it qualificatory remarks devised to reduce its apparent seriousness or at least offer some form of "hope."

While in some Cohen circumstances news of a death was "broken gently," in most of the announcements of death I observed that was not done. In the DOA cases on which my observations of death announcements were made, physicians feel obliged to deliver news of a death immediately. "Breaking news gently" as an act of anticipatory comforting seems proper only for those who have some degree of intimacy with the recipient, or, as for example in the case of clergymen, some extended role in the post-announcement reaction of the bereaved. The hospital physician has few appropriate resources in such situations and has his task essentially circumscribed as the delivery of the news alone. It can be speculatively suggested that those close to the event's occurrence itself,

so situated that questions of their own responsibility might arise, run
some risk in attempting to soften the delivery of news, should that imply
a greater concern for the bereaved then that which existed for the patient.[8] In the County situation, deaths were felt to require immediate
informing and when a proper announcer was not available, attempts were
made to isolate the unknowledgeable bereaved as quickly as possible, as
much to minimize the emotional pressures felt by the staff as to give
privacy to the scene to follow. The relative is escorted to a private room,
if one is available, and told to await the doctor's arrival. This is done to
guarantee that he will not unwittingly engage others in interaction or be
unwittingly so engaged by others, whether those others know of the
death but are not permitted to announce such matters (e.g., nurses, aides,
clerks, administrative personnel) or are unaware that the bereaved-to-be
is such.

An additional warrant for isolating such persons, at County particularly, derives from the character of ward social structure. Information about recently occurring deaths is not always transmitted to all
personnel in secrecy, as I have pointed out above, so there always exists
the possibility that the occurrence of a death will be learned of by one
staff member in his conversation with another, and such conversation is
not always discreetly conducted in safe backstage areas. A bereaved-
to-be might overhear such a conversation in the circumstance where the
person reporting the death and the person learning of it do not know
the relative, or where there is at least one party to an interaction who is
unfamiliar with the bereaved-to-be and talks of the death in his presence.
In one instance, a morgue attendant was observed to arrive at the nurses'
desk to secure a deceased patient's belongings and addressed the nurse,
asking where the patient's things were, while the relative was standing
alongside the nurses' station awaiting the physician. The nurse managed,
by eye signal, to alert the attendant to the bystander's identity and inhibit further references to his relative's body. This sort of possibility is
maximized when the news of a death spreads within the hospital to those
occupationally involved in such matters faster than it spreads to kin, a
situation particularly prevalent in County. The fact that bodies are

[8] For a fictional account of an especially extended delivery of news of a death by
an army chaplain, see N. Mailer, *The Naked and the Dead* (New York: Signet Books,
1958), pp. 207–208:

"Go ahead and smoke son . . . you get much mail from home . . . son
I have some pretty bad news for you . . . you know son, there're a lot
of things which are difficult to understand. You just have to believe that
it's right, and that there's a good reason for it, that God understands and
sees and does what is best, even if we don't understand right away."
". . . my wife didn't leave me did she?"
". . . no son but there's been a death. . . ."

wrapped up before their dismissal from the ward bed, presumably a practice motivated by sanitation, seems at least possibly due, as well, to the
fact that there are never complete safeguards to prevent a relative of the
deceased patient whose body is being brought down the hall from otherwise directly identifing his relative.

Several special safeguards are employed to minimize the likelihood
of indirect discoveries and improper conversational developments. One
practice in wide use is to organize the arrival of the relative so that
he will clearly be expected and proper preparations will have been taken
in advance. This is typically the practice at Cohen Hospital, where it is
felt more advisable for members of the family to be informed of the
death in person. Frequently, a nurse calls the family and informs them
that the "patient has taken a turn for the worse and the doctor advises
you to come to the hospital." An alternative procedure, occasionally employed at Cohen, is for the nurse to call the family and advise them that
the "doctor said he wanted to talk with you and wanted to know where
you could be reached"; this is done in the circumstance where nurses
cannot locate the private physician and want to be able to keep tabs on
the relatives' whereabouts. From the standpoint of the hospital the most
easily managed deaths—those requiring the least amount of scrutiny of
arriving members of the public—are those which occur at late evening
hours. From the physician's standpoint, given his required attention to
such events and inability to delegate their care to others, nighttime
deaths are inconvenient insofar as he is awakened and must see the
family, but more convenient than the daytime death that ties him up at
the hospital or on the telephone awaiting the chance to contact members
of the family.

Another practice is for nurses, on their own initiative, to call the
physician to inform him of the death and then inform families of the
need to come to the hospital. They thus provide for the physician's
having control over the family's whereabouts and try to avoid the circumstance where, once the physician arrives, the family might not be
able to be reached, or might unexpectedly and unknowingly arrive at
the hospital before the physician does. Timing is an important consideration: nurses learn from doctors when the latter plan to arrive at the
hospital and time their calls to the families so that family members will
arrive after the physician does.

❧❧❧ THE ANNOUNCEMENT OF DEATH:
Conversational Methods for the Handling of Grief

The announcement-of-death occasions I shall now examine in detail were mainly those generated by the DOA circumstance, explored in

Chapter 4, at County Hospital. They involved, as their participants, a family member whose relative had just died and was not a hospital patient and an intern or resident on duty in County's Emergency Unit, who had no prior acquaintance with the family or the deceased before death. Of the 52 observed DOA cases where I witnessed the announcement of death, 34 were the deaths of white persons and 18 of Negroes. Forty-one cases involved persons over 50 years of age, 7 were people between 18 and 42, and 6 were children. From information gathered by the coroner (who has the responsibility for legal identification and medical investigation of deaths when they occur outside the hospital or within 24 hours after hospital admission), of the 31 cases with available occupational histories, 6 were professional people, 15 white collar workers and small businessmen, 7 skilled laborers, and 3 unskilled workers. As the Emergency Unit serves as a general facility for ambulance cases of an "emergency" character and is not restricted to persons with limited incomes, the social class characteristics of DOA persons are considerably more various, and generally more middle-class, than those of the hospital's general patient population.[9]

The occasion of the announcement, in this situation, typically is generated in the following way: a member of the family arrives at the Emergency Unit shortly after the ambulance's arrival, having been told to come to the Unit by policemen or ambulance drivers. In many instances the family member was called from work, in others he was present at the scene of the ambulance pickup, perhaps responsible for notification of the police or ambulance service himself. In these latter circumstances, he might be in a position to know directly, in detail, what it is that has transpired. When not present at the scene but telephoned or otherwise informed to come to the hospital, his expectations may not be clearly formulated. He may have received, by way of notification, the instruction, "Your wife has been in an accident and has been taken to County Hospital," or the notification might have included any other variant degree of information. When he arrives at the hospital, his expectation is more or less formulated depending upon his own presence at the accident, his knowledge of the person's prior health, the information he has been provided by drivers and police and other sources. While the fact of having been called into the hospital clearly delimits the range of expectable happenings, what the alternatives are may be unclear.

Physicians believe that incoming relatives, whether or not they have clear expectations that a death has occurred or attend such a

---

[9] On occasion a DOA case is attended by a private physician who has been called to the hospital, and it is he who announces the death to the family. My observations are based entirely on cases where a staff doctor made the announcement.

possibility, must be informed of the death. The physician does not consider it warrant for not telling him when the recipient-to-be appears, in the manner of his demeanor, to "already know." There exists the strongly felt obligation that as quickly upon his arrival at the hospital as is possible, the relative will be escorted to a private room and the death's occurrence be announced.[10] Despite the lack of any actual medical intervention in the usual DOA case, hospital personnel are always sensitive to the possible responses of relatives to the institutionalized definition of the setting and their possible claims that its performers have some rightful responsibility for such matters as the occurrence of deaths. By sheer virtue of his location in the social structure, as well as the hospital's, the physician experiences the obligation to behave with some degree of accountability for the occurrence of an event beyond his ecologically accessible jurisdiction, involving a set of persons with whom no contractual duties had been undertaken, and a corpse whose previous breathing, generally speaking, was never witnessed. By the fact of a death somewhere in the neighboring streets or residences, and the corpse's delivery to his station, he must, at least for a short while, assume the status of a committed, involved party.[11]

The general procedure is for the clerk at the admissions desk rapidly to escort the family member to a small office immediately opposite the entrance way, instruct him to await the arrival of the doctor, and close the door behind him. Personnel at this station, usually a clerk and a nurse, attend the impending arrival of the DOA's relatives and seek to locate them quickly once they arrive. It is generally the case that family members in such situations announce their identities immediately upon their arrival, their concern apparently being that news be rapidly obtained, i.e., that staff members be able to locate them when they have the news. The anxiousness they generally evidence serves to place personnel on guard in their presence, a caution which would be more difficult to exercise and more disruptive of work routines were relatives to arrive nonchalantly on the scene. This caution is of particularly great importance when the person whose death has been pronounced is not readily identifiable, e.g., when he carries no wallet identification, for here the sheer fact of a relative's name provides no basis for matching

[10] This—a death—was the only occurrence at County Hospital in which a private room was used for conversation between staff members and patients' families.

[11] This *de facto* implication is, of course, one notorious aspect in which the physician's tasks and interactional possibilities in delivering bad news differ from those other bearers of sad tidings, such as the telegraph delivery boy and, somewhat less distinctly, the policeman. While the physician can and does avoid street accident scenes, the hospital's definition as a public place and the intern or resident's employment in it brings the street inside. As a physician, he cannot, like the telegram deliverer, merely present the news and leave the scene, but must evidence some degree of general concern and responsibility.

deceased and bereaved. Generally, given the history of events in the Unit, the clerk expects that following the occurrence of a DOA, there will arrive a person who appears particularly anxious. If a name is available for the dead person, with the announcement by the relative of his name the match is made. It is common for relatives to announce, in addition to their names, their relation to the person about whom they seek information and, furthermore, some piece of information about the generation of the event which will serve additionally to match the two parties, e.g., "I'm Mr. S., I was told to come here because they brought my son in," "Did they just bring in an elderly woman? I'm her daughter."

It is of interest to note that no errors were ever made, nor were any reported by staff members, in the matching of deceased to relative, and that this alignment occurs without any visual body identification procedure of the sort that occurs when bodies are in the custody of the police or coroner. The mere announcement of a name, or, in several cases where no identification was available on the deceased, no more than a remark such as "I was told to come about my father," was taken as warrant that the match had correctly been established, whereupon announcement of the death was made. No additional attempt was made, in any case prior to the announcement, to insure specifically that the death which the physician was to announce was the death of a party about whom the relative in question sought information.[12]

It is an extremely interesting fact about death, one which I cannot fully explore here, that persons generally have, with respect to the procedures of identifying the body and the pronouncement of death, complete and absolute trust that those procedures have been correctly undertaken. Apparently there is complete confidence that those social arrangements which produced the news are without defects, that the person who arrives at the hospital claiming that his father was brought there is, in fact, the son of the man who was brought there and pronounced dead; that the dissemination of news from the ambulance driver to the policeman to the wife at home, which results in her coming to the hospital, was errorless; that the physician who read from the identification card in the wallet a

---

[12] When body identification is requested, as is done in the coroner's office, that identification is generally not a precondition for notifying others of that person's death, nor is identification employed as the means of notification. In the greatest number of "identifications," the coroner reported, persons are not told "would you come to the coroner's office to identify a body," or "we think your wife died and we want you to come to identify this body and see if it is your wife." Rather, I was told, the identification of bodies is put as a legally required formality, and officials will not qualify their announcements of death pending that legal identification. In the greatest number of coroner cases bereavement has already begun before the relative comes to the county morgue to make the identification.

man's name and telephoned the wife of that man, did not make a mistaken reading.

This "clarity" is best seen in the announcement scene itself, when the news of the death is delivered. Once the occurrence of the death is announced by the physician, the recipient of the news does not attempt to question, deny, revise, undermine, or protest the physician's assertion in any of the ways that persons routinely use to question, deny, revise, undermine, and protest assertions purporting the occurrence of an event. Once the death's happening is reported, none of the interchange to follow addresses the validity of the purported fact. Rather, what follows in the way of crying, sobbing, moaning, and then "talking"—the sequence of which I shall shortly discuss—is directly given by the unquestioned, commonly agreed upon status of the event being cried, sobbed, moaned, and "talked" about.[13] Once said, the reported upon fact stands thereafter as a permanently correct assertion that apparently needs no documentation or explanation to convince the relative of its actual occurrence. With the doctor's opening words, bereavement occurs. In no instances did recipients voice concern that perhaps an error in identification had been made, that perhaps the pronouncement of death was not accurately conducted, and the like. Consider the available and commonly used institutionalized procedures for demanding to see evidence, seeking consultation from others, obtaining proper credentials from a reporter of news, in other circumstances. Persons regularly use, in medical and nonmedical settings, their knowledge of the bureaucratically organized conditions of work for circumventing and doubting assertions of policy and fact, yet in no announcement-of-death occasion was it asked: "Have you enough knowledge to make such assessments?" or "Let me talk to your superior about this." Claims as to the professional competence of a reporter of news or witness of affairs, as well as his personal motives and interests, are routinely made to discredit or evaluate the events he purports correctly to report upon, e.g., in the legal system, in the treatment of medical diagnoses of serious illnesses where consultation is sought from others, etc.

Death seems to be a paradigmatic example of what might be termed a "clear social fact." Persons have complete and unquestioned faith in the

---

[13] There is a common form of "disbelief" which purportedly occurs with some frequency among bereaved persons. Bereaved persons have been reported to go through periods where they engage in conversations with their deceased relatives, set the dinner table for them, and otherwise refuse to "accept" the fact of the death. These clinical varieties of disbelief were not observed in the reactions to the news of death in the hospital. Whatever might have been the later cognitive orientations of relatives with respect to the death's occurrence, in the hospital no expressions of disbelief of this radical character were observed. Such forms of disbelief are to be distinguished from expressions of incredulity, which were very common, e.g., "I just can't believe it," "it doesn't seem real," "he was so young it just doesn't make sense," etc.

social organization of medical inquiry which produces proclamations of death, so that for the physician to announce that a person is dead makes it so. While doubts are regularly held with respect to the medical man's competence in the diagnosis of disease, no doubts are raised with respect to his ability to identify death. It is not clear, nor is there any basis for arguing the matter, that it is the physician's authority that provides the fact of a death which he announces with its unquestioned status as a correctly decided matter, nor is there any basis for assigning to the manner of his delivery of news of death a prominent role in the establishment of that correctness. Unfortunately no evidence is available which would permit us to answer the questions: What if the hospital janitor were to announce the death?, What if the physician were to announce it with hesitancy?, e.g., "We think your father died," or "It is our opinion that your father died." The conditions for the "clarity" of this piece of news cannot be offered, though it is to be noted that physicians, in their announcements of death, do so with authority and complete surety, and that other staff members are not permitted to make such announcements. I would suspect that were the physician to say, "We think your father died," this way of delivery would be most upsetting to a recipient, and that persons expect, with respect to death, that there is no question whatsoever, that one is or one isn't, an expectation which seems to operate for only a few matters, another of which, in the hospital, appears to be the sex of a newborn.[14]

With respect to body identification and bereaved–deceased matching, it is to be noted that the conditions for faith in the correctness of such procedures have been undermined, as for example during times of war, when it becomes commonplace for the possibility of error to be attended even after a body has purportedly been located. In large-scale accidents, involving large numbers of persons, body identification and claiming becomes a required task of relatives, one which is regarded as essential before the establishment of a proper match is warranted.[15] With respect at least to singly occurring deaths and those the determination of which is decided by a physician, persons have a remarkable faith in the fact that about such matters errors are not made. What makes this faith particularly remarkable is that in the case of the DOA death, a completely unknown physician, one with whom no personalized basis of trust exists, has his proclamations, of great importance for the family, unquestionably, immediately, and unthinkingly taken, and once made, as

[14] Although here we observe the curious practice of holding up an infant in the hospital nursery and purposefully exposing its genitals, so that parents can have a look for themselves.

[15] For a vivid account of such a situation in a hospital setting, see S. R. Cutolo, *Bellevue Is My Home* (Garden City: Doubleday & Company, Inc., 1956), Chapter XV, "Identity Unknown."

thereby, on their face value, indubitably correct. While entrustment to others of matters of lesser significance is routinely made only upon investigation, and only provisionally, the entitlement to determination of a death, and the death of a correct party, is given without reservation. A complete stranger, the hospital physician, becomes, in a sense, the most intimate and entrusted of persons.

Let me now turn to the details of the announcement-of-death occasion, taking up the analysis with the opening lines of this encounter and exploring the unfolding structure of the occasion. In announcing the death, the physician makes his announcement forthrightly, with no circuity in the conduct of the delivery of the actual news. By the manner of his seriousness when he enters the scene, he seems effectively to inhibit any byplay between relatives or overtures directed toward him. Relatives were observed to sit quietly as he began to talk, no questions were initially asked, no exchanges of politenesses seen. The scene became defined, from the first moment, as an occasion of utmost seriousness. Generally, the doctor's announcement of the death was made within the first or first two sentences, usually in the course of one long sentence. An interesting feature of his presentation, more common in the DOA situation than in announcements of deaths of hospital patients, was that in announcing the death he provided, in some way, that the death be presented as having followed a course of "dying." In nearly every scene I witnessed, the doctor's opening remarks contained an historical reference. Some examples were:

> Mrs. Jones, apparently Mr. Jones had a heart attack this afternoon and his body was too weak to fight it and he passed away.
>
> It seems that in this accident your son's chest was broken and a rib probably punctured the heart area and he could not survive that kind of injury.
>
> Your husband apparently had a stroke or heart attack and his system was not capable of surviving through it. He passed away before he reached the hospital.
>
> It seems that there must have been a massive rupture of the heart, Mrs. Smith. Your husband died upon arrival at the hospital.
>
> From what we can tell it appears as though he must have been suffering from a heart ailment and apparently this time the attack was too strong for his system.

In none of the instances I observed was the relative told of the death in a sentence that included no reference to some medically relevant causal antecedent. This was true in accident as well as "natural" deaths, and true whether or not the physician had any basis for assuming a likely cause of death. The greatest proportion of DOA cases are known to be heart attack victims, and in the event that there was no accident, nor any sign which would obviously rule out a heart attack, the physician generally says, "We're not sure but it might have been a heart attack," or some other remark containing reference to a likely cause. There were no instances of simply, "Your husband died," without qualifying, causally relevant additions. Physicians seem to feel in such situations that historicizing their delivery of news, no matter how much their limited knowledge of the case may restrict the range of possibilities, helps not only reduce some of the shock value of "sudden deaths" but aids in the very grasp of the news. The correctness of the physician's supposed cause of death is of secondary significance relative to the sheer fact that he provides some sequential formulation of its generation, some means whereby the occurrence can be placed in a sequence of natural or accidental events. This is felt particularly to be necessary in the DOA circumstance, where many deaths occur with no apparent "reason," particularly the so-called "sudden unexpected deaths," not uncommon among young adults.[16] It seems to be the case that physicians feel that persons require (and perhaps themselves as well), for a beginning comprehension of what it is that occurred, some causally portrayed version.

After the death has been announced, generally within the first sentence of the physician's talk, there occurs, characteristically, a period in which the physician remains silent and the relative engages in some display of shock, dismay, disorientation, and the like. Comparing the extent and form of emotional responses to announcements of death in various circumstances, I found a considerable amount of variability. On some occasions there was no crying whatever; the doctor's mention of the death was responded to with downward looking silence. On other occasions, his utterance "passed away," or "died" spontaneously produced hysterical crying, screaming, moaning, trembling, etc. I have observed relatives, particularly women, fall to the floor, loudly moaning and crying (as, it seems, Negro women know how to do especially well), intermittently cursing, shaking, and screaming. In numerous instances I have seen men and women tear at themselves, pulling their hair, tugging at their garments, biting their lips.

The form of the initial reaction to the death's announcement, both in its over-all tonal character and duration, is fairly well predictable. A combination of the following attributes would expectably be attended by a thoroughly explosive response: a young, only child's sudden accidental death announced to his or her young Negro mother. At the other end of a possible continuum of expressive behavior, the announcement of a long-term chronically ill, white Protestant woman's death to her upper-middle-

---

[16] For a discussion of "sudden unexpected deaths," see C. Richter, "The Phenomenon of Unexplained Sudden Death in Animals and Man," in H. Feifel, ed., *The Meaning of Death* (New York: McGraw-Hill Book Company, 1959), pp. 302–313.

class nephew, would likely be characterized by a considerably less apparent extent of affectual trauma.

Differences in emotional response are predictable by physicians and nurses and are explained by them through reference to a variety of common-sense sociological and psychiatric bereavement theories. Typically invoked causal accounts involve reference to: *1.* subcultural, racial definitions of appropriate grief, *2.* family social structure, *3.* the generalized social loss value of the deceased, *4.* expectability of the death as an independent variable, *5.* psychoanalytical theories of guilt, etc. Physicians' and nurses' theories of bereavement behavior, like their professional counterparts, are generally multivariate, containing references to mutually influential variables, e.g., "guilt and the Negro family structure."

Lay sociological and psychiatric interpretations of grieving occur, in the hospital, as predominantly extramural theorizing. Nurses and physicians overhear the crying of a woman behind the closed door and talk among themselves about the reasons for the form it takes. There is considerable bull-session interpretation of variations in emotional response to death, and hospital personnel often invoke their own experiences with death as elaborations or support of their theories. A good deal of this interpretation involves moral judgments as well, e.g., "These Negroes don't know how to control themselves," "Now, that's taking it like a man."

For important reasons, however, the expectations staff members hold of the relative's likely response to the news of the death do not directly enter to structure the character of the announcement occasion and the doctor's activity in it. While experienced physicians do come to expect differences in response, and orient their manner of informing somewhat in light of the news' expectable reception (e.g., they regard the task of having to inform a young mother of her child's death as more touchy and fraught with unpleasantness than the announcement of an older person's death), there are definite limits on the extent to which they can employ such expectations to structure and interaction in the setting.

A presumption of moral integrity is granted the immediately bereaved which, at least for a reasonable time period, is not considered to be invalidated should his behavior and appearance appear inconsistent with his status. The immediately bereaved who does not cry or engage in other recognizeable displays of grief, must nonetheless be regarded as grievous. This is clearly indicated in our tendency to characterize such persons as those who "take it well," the implication clearly being that they are "taking it," but "showing it" less obviously. A key problem in interacting with newly bereaved persons, particularly at the very beginning of the death announcement occasion, but generally confronted in a wide variety of situations, is the detection of that point in an encounter at which time it is permissible to regard them as having the capacity and desire to show respect for normally constituted forms of interaction. This problem resides in the fact that any overture to interaction can be taken as premature, its prematurity lying in the possibility that the bereaved is not yet to be held to respect some orderly form of interaction as governing his conduct.

With the announcement of a death and the creation of his status as a bereaved person, the relative enjoys the right at least temporarily to suspend his concern for normally enforceable requirements of demeanor, attentiveness, grace, deference, respect for the setting, in sum, with a properly situated composure. He can, in Goffman's terms, "flood out,"[17] without fear of being sanctioned for so doing. He has a right to expect that others will respect his position. This poses an interactive problem, which is constituted by the fact that there exists no easily employed rule for assessing the relation between the bereaved's appearances and his "state of mind"; appearances of calmness cannot readily be taken to represent the recipient's emotional composure. This ambiguity of appearances is seen in the everpresent threat that the appearance of composure constitutes *merely an appearance,* and any effort to take the appearance as corresponding to an underlying composure might be met with the response which says, "you have a lot of nerve to regard me as calm just because I don't show my grief." An example of such a response appeared in the *San Francisco Chronicle,* where the husband of a murdered woman, perhaps because of his own possible implication in her death, is reported to have said: "I'm outwardly calm because I'm taking sedatives. Inside I'm grieving more than anyone will ever know."[18]

Let me depart from the main concern with the interaction structure of the announcement occasion, to comment briefly on some general aspects of this interpretative ambiguity. This problem is differently experienced in different points in the course of bereavement and is more or less troublesome depending upon the relationship between the immediately bereaved and other interactants. In the announcement-of-death scene itself, at a point so close to the receipt of the news, nonbereaved persons feel difficulty in engaging the immediately bereaved in any talk whatsoever. The bereaved is, at this point and at least for a short while thereafter, entitled to nearly complete disregard for proprieties governing interactive presence. That right, to be "out of it," is of short duration however, and persons unable to "pull themselves together"

[17] E. Goffman, *Encounters* (Indianapolis: The Bobbs-Merrill Co., Inc., 1961), pp. 55–61.

[18] December, 1963. The bereaved's right to grieve, while rather freely given, is not altogether immune to attack. The requirement to give the account cited above is evidence that such rights must be somewhat earned, and that persons who find it difficult or impossible to produce tears may be deeply troubled by what that says about their sense of loss.

with reasonable rapidity, or at least refrain from public crying, will soon be the object of medical and psychiatric treatment as well as less masked forms of sanctioning. During periods following the first days of the death, the problem of the bereaved's readiness to interact and the proper use of an inferential apparatus in the interpretation of his appearances, takes on a different character. What seems to happen is that immediately bereaved persons are regarded as persons with whom it is improper to engage in sociable conversation, to treat in conversation matters of everyday life. The bereaved is regarded as one for whom appropriate talk is to be restricted to "death relevant matters," albeit within the clearly delimited structure of sympathy engagements. For what can be a long time after a death, persons tread carefully in interaction with the immediately bereaved, exhibiting caution in initiating talk about matters of general conversational value.

In American society particularly, where bereaved persons do not wear visible insignia of their grief, it is a continually problematic matter both for them and others as to the proper relevance of their own status as an attendable matter in conversation. Bereaved persons have expressed the view that while they often seek to have their status as bereaved lose its prominence as a way others attend them, others feel obliged to take their cues from the bereaved before undertaking nonsympathetic conversation. Bereaved persons have reported that a great advantage in having persons close to one nearby is that with them, those who share their status as bereaved, one can talk about other things. It is characteristic for bereaved persons to take first action in relieving pressure on the nonbereaved, which they frequently do, for example, by purposefully directing conversation to matters concerning the nonbereaved. What sympathy phone calls I have managed to overhear all seem to have the prevalent feature that there is a forced distribution of interest, whereby after the offer of sympathy has been made, the bereaved directs a question to the sympathizer, e.g., "How are your children these days?" or otherwise attempts to remove from the center of attention the fact of his own bereaved status by making small talk and the like.

Bereaved persons apparently have considerable difficulty in their management of the proprieties of their own situation. They frequently don't know at what point they should undertake activities typically engaged in prior to the death, and a large part of their difficulty derives from the sheer fact of their known status as a bereaved, which leaves them open to being treated sorrowfully no matter how they might conduct themselves. It is felt that only with time do they lose their status as bereaved in the eyes of others and cease to encounter treatments as a grievous person, and that time can often come long after they have ceased regarding themselves in that fashion. The proprieties governing the treatment of persons so situated continually place upon them the burden of demonstrating their readiness for normal treatment.

A contrary strain operates at the same time, namely that in antici-pation of the sympathy gestures of others, the bereaved feels obliged to appear sufficiently grievous as to warrant those offers of condolences. Bereaved find it necessary to attend the fact that for others their be-reavement may be more relevant than for themselves, these others not being in a position properly to assume that the impact of the death has lost its force. The anticipation of treatment by others as a bereaved operates to keep the bereaved in a bereaved status, at least in his public encounters. This phenomenon is clearly seen with respect to the use of the telephone, for here particularly the bereaved may have little control over getting involved with a would-be sympathizer. Be-reaved persons have reported that they find it necessary, often for an extended period of time after the death, to answer the phone with a sufficiently grave tone to appear properly deserving of the sympathy a caller may be about to offer, not wanting such a person to be caught off guard with a pleasant "hello" and left with nothing to say or made to feel particularly awkward.

It can be argued that a key function of those social gatherings that occur shortly after the time of death is to expedite the process of receiving incoming gestures of sympathy. Without such gatherings, par-ticularly in the case of bereaved who are well-known in the community, many more sympathizers must be encountered one by one, over an extended period of time after the death, and the more removed a contact of this sort from the time of the death, the more work must go into the mutual management of the death's relevance for conversa-tion about it. (Attendance at the funeral does not appear to relieve a sympathizer from his obligation to offer condolences, for that offer must generally be made in a more direct and personal fashion.) A stand-ard additional practice, in American society—one which, in some sense, substitutes for the practice of wearing visible insignia of mourning—is for the immediately bereaved to go into isolation for a period of time sufficiently extensive so that upon his re-emergence into public life the relevance of the death has dissipated and both he and others can manage ordinary interaction with less strain.

Before returning to the announcement-of-death occasion in the hospital, a comment about the sociological analysis of grieving behavior seems warranted. There has been a tendency in the (limited) sociological literature on grief, to place a one-sided emphasis on the role of normative elements in expressive behavior. Durkheim's classic statement sets the tone for this emphasis:

> . . . mourning is not the spontaneous expression of individual emo-tions . . . mourning is not a natural movement of private feelings

> wounded by cruel loss; it is a duty imposed by the group. One
> weeps, not simply because he is sad, but because he is forced to
> weep. It is a ritual attitude which he is forced to adopt . . . but
> which is, in a large measure, independent of his affective state.[19]

It can be warrantably said, I believe, that a vulgar, not uncommon reading of Durkheim readily implies a debunking, degrading, and discrediting view of the bereaved person. Despite Durkheim's weak reservation: "not simply because he is sad," the dominant tone of the "normative" perspective, improperly implied in this and other instances, can be extended as follows: people cry because it is expected of them that they cry; they are not really as upset or disoriented as their behavior would imply; people are basically fakes in a normative order. It is not a far step, given an emphasis which one-sidedly says: persons' actual emotions are probably less severe than the normatively appropriate mode of expression requires, to debunking bereaved persons and eliminating the possibility of "genuine grief."

While I am by no means suggesting suspension of interest in normatively prescribed expressive modes, nor a generalized humanist stance, I am proposing that a more sophisticated mode of analysis is required if one wishes to assess the actual operation of "expectations." Consider the following possibility (which I believe to be frequently the case): persons express considerably less grief than they actually experience, particularly in semipublic encounters with relative strangers like the hospital physician, and for that matter, at a funeral, for prescribed and available cultural models for appropriate expressiveness may be severely limiting, requiring a through and through curtailment on actually experienced feelings of loss. So that the relative might say of the relation between the appearances he is presenting and the grief he "actually feels": it is impossible for you to know what it is like; I'm crying all right but you can't imagine how little that says about my feelings.

Fortunately, Durkheim's statement, properly read, need not be simplistically and discreditingly applied, but, in its general terms, permits of any of a wide range of possible interpretations of the relationship between presented appearances and underlying sentiment. Persons who are apparently obliging an order of crying in the hospital or walking down the street can be viewed as in fact standing in any of a variety of relations to their apparent activities, e.g., one of cynicism, sarcasm, mocking, feigning, underplaying, dramatizing. They can be viewed, when composed, as merely obliging the order or actually composed, and when upset, as merely obliging the requirements for demonstrating upsettedness, upset to a degree commensurate with what appears, or upset far in excess of their apparent display of grief.

[19] E. Durkheim, *Elementary Forms of Religious Life* (New York: Free Press of Glencoe, Inc., 1947), p. 397.

It is a central feature of bereavement situations that the rule-governed character of expressive behavior is precisely its most problematic aspect. In the routinization of contacts between bereaved and nonbereaved persons we see continuous work involved in the adjustment of actual feelings to the conditions of concrete interactional situations, wherein there is a considerable amount both of underplaying and overplaying of expressive demonstration, required to handle the conditions of interaction between parties holding varying perspectives toward the death. The fact that knowledge and use of the proprieties becomes problematic for bereaved and nonbereaved has its basis in the fact that the temporally graded social definitions of the status *bereaved* establish conditions of ambiguity. A view of bereavement behavior adequate to description of the circumstances grieving entails in the case of a society in which a whole range of contacts occur, from those involving the most intimate of relations to those involving the merely acquainted, must treat the essentially troublesome character of the normative elements in grief. Persons are engaged, so it seems, in the continual de-emphasis of their feelings of loss, out of respect for the difficulties of interaction facing those less intimately involved in the death than themselves. It is such de-emphasis, the underlying obligations for which concern the requirements of ordinary conversational discourse, that available notions of grieving as "culturally appropriate" fail to handle, for such notions ignore the situational and interactional determinants of the limits of grieving behavior.

In the doctor-relative encounter, the problem of adjusting feelings so that interaction may proceed is most marked, particularly in the DOA circumstance involving persons whose only basis for interaction is the occasion of the death that brings them together. The manner of this adjustment has, as its most prominent feature, the fact that the bereaved takes the physician off the hook, spares him the discomfort of witnessing the bereaved's pain, and does so by agreeing to engage in relatively nonemotional interaction. It can be argued that this setting stands as a training session wherein the bereaved person learns what it will be like to deal with those for whom the death can have nowhere near the significance it has for himself, a problem he will continually face in his encounters with a wide range of others. In the course of the bereavement career, it is the first of a series of polite engagements, wherein the conditions of interaction require appropriate modulation of sentiments and appropriate regard for the other's situation of discomfort. Let me now examine the way in which this adjustment occurs.

The bereaved's right to a temporary "awayness" is respected by the physician, who must tread carefully in initiating any interaction lest that initiation appear premised on the recipient's "recovery," an assumption that the recipient might not want made about his behavior. This places the burden of initiating interaction largely on the recipient of the news. While the informed relative is actively engaged in crying, weeping, sobbing, or moaning, the doctor maintains as passive a stance as the fact of his presence will allow. He looks away, or downwardly, and says nothing. Occasionally physicians employ the procedure of turning around, leaving their backs to the crying relative. The doctor doesn't smoke, nor does he look over any papers he might have in his hands. Neither does he exhibit any marked casualness in demeanor, like propping a foot up on a chair or table. He usually remains silently standing.

In none of the cases I have observed did the physician touch the relative or attempt to say anything while the relative was crying. No sympathy remarks or gestures of sorrow were offered during the earliest period following his announcement (sometimes the announcement is phrased sympathetically, e.g., "I'm sorry to have to tell you that your father passed away this morning"; at the end of the encounter, the physician often takes leave of the relatives with "I'm sorry"). During telephone call announcements of death, if the relative sobs or cries loudly, or remains silent, the doctor remains silent himself.

While no sympathy gestures are made, neither does the doctor withdraw from the scene altogether by leaving the room, as, for example, does the telegram delivery boy. The doctor is concerned that the scene be contained and that he have some control over its progress, that it not, for example, follow him out into the hall. In nearly all cases the first genuine interchange of remarks was initiated by the relative. During the period of crying, if there is any, relatives frequently "talk." Examples are: "I can't believe it," "It's just not fair," "Goddamn," "Not John . . . no. . . ." These remarks are not responded to as they are not addressed to anyone. Frequently, they are punctuated by crying. The physician remains silent.

With relatives who do not express audible signs of despair, there is, at the outset, a system of mutual disattending as well. The relative looks away from the doctor and the doctor avoids confronting the relative's line of vision. There is usually in such instances a prolonged period of silence, during which mutual disattending occurs.

It is useful to consider the role of embarrassment in this setting. As I have mentioned above, it constitutes no warrant for withholding information about another's death just because the knowledgeable person wishes to avoid embarrassing the uniformed by forcibly bringing him to tears. The physician has the problem of having to relate the occurrence of the death, minimizing the possibility that the relative will become embarrassed by his crying and, at the same time, insure that he retain control over the occasion. While he isolates the affair from the visibility of onlookers, he himself occupies somewhat of the position of an outsider; yet he cannot remove himself from the setting and still accomplish other tasks, e.g., instructing relatives regarding funeral obligations, obtaining an autopsy permit (in hospital patient deaths), and generally controlling the encounter so that it doesn't generate into an explosive scene. While persons appear readily able to cry spontaneously in the presence of a stranger when delivered news of a death, and while embarrassment must not be made to inhibit performance of the informer's task, it seems that the potentiality for embarrassment still strongly exists, and public crying can be sustained for only a rather short period of time before the cryer senses not only his own embarrassment but that which he is creating for others by not being able to isolate himself from them effectively and thereby release them from having to witness his grief.

The point at which genuine verbal interaction reoccurs is initiated at that moment when the relative can provide some demonstration of his own readiness to undertake discourse. Persons who do not cry can be seen to engage in various maneuvers the central strategy of which resides in building into their behavior the possibility that a shift will be detectable in it, that shift constituting an appropriate indication of their readiness to move from crying to other matters. So, for example, some persons made it a point to look away or turn around or lower their heads after they were informed of the death, allowing them later to realign their eyes and bodies to meet the physician's awaiting presence. In this, the physician assists them, himself looking away to make it easier for them to withdraw and then return. The recipient of the news seems to take it that he cannot merely rely on his momentary presentational composure, that in itself not providing, at the outset, sufficient basis for the physician to regard him as "recovered" or "not upset." Some more positive demonstration of readiness, as with the use of a sequence, must be employed.

The initiation of "talk" usually properly begins the integration to orderly interaction, and the physician maintains himself ready to accept such a demonstration of readiness while, at the same time, allowing for initial failures in it. Should the recipient attempt to start to say something and burst anew into tears, the doctor acts as though the attempt were never made.

Frequently, the recipient's first attempt will utilize his own embarrassment and the uneasiness he preceives he is creating for the doctor, e.g., via an apology for "carrying on so." If the apology is accompanied by a commensurate degree of actual composure, which the physician detects as potentially stable, he will assure the recipient that "no apologies are necessary." This exchange can then serve to provide the first bridge toward a realignment of mutually oriented activity. Generally, the physician tends to be over-cautious and prefers to wait as long as possible before accepting a gesture of readiness. In one case with which I am familiar, a man was told of his mother's death and exhibited absolutely no alteration in his appearance or composure. The man instead came right back with "I was expecting it to happen soon," in quite flat, unemotional, and forthright tones; he didn't flinch at all and there was no apparent sorrow in his remark. The physician appeared uneasy and simply looked down at the floor. Gradually, the man followed him by looking downward, covered his head with his arms, and remained silent for about a minute. Then he looked up, as simultaneously did the doctor, and made an opening remark. For a moment or two there was a considerable strain as the physician attempted to regard the man as somewhat unaware of what was told to him. Rather than repeat the announcement, he employed his own body to indicate his respect for the bereaved and the situation of bereavement, and the "bereaved" man followed in turn to act in appreciation.

"Talk" typically begins with an overture by the relative for some form of information. While there seems to be no particular preference for order, the following items were raised in a very great majority of cases:

1. *The matter of cause:* In the DOA circumstance particularly, the relative is likely to begin by asking, in one or another version, "Why did he die, doctor?" This occurred despite the fact that the doctor's announcement of the death contained an historical, causally couched reference to the death. In general medical ward deaths, especially with patients whose condition had been a previous topic of conversation between the doctor and relative, the physician will often raise issue of cause by restating a previous diagnosis, now posed as the most likely interpretation of the death. The following remark, recorded from a telephone announcement, is typical of this way of introducing the issue of cause:

> Apparently his heart became particularly strained during the night and, as we expected he might, he must have had another attack. As you know he was very weak and that's why his system couldn't tolerate this new attack.

In responding to the DOA relative's query about why he died, the announcing doctors often attempted to propose a tentative answer and then ask some questions themselves. The particular status of these questions is extremely important for my analysis. The physician will often respond to a query about "why" with a remark on the order of "from the looks of it, he seemed to have had a general heart attack," and then ask a question like the following actual one:

> Did your father have a history of heart attacks?
> Yes, for about twelve years.

whereupon the subject of prior illness was dropped. Another doctor asked the relative of a DOA:

Had your wife been under the care of a physician?

To which the husband answered:

For about seven months now. She was in the hospital for three weeks early in April.

The subject of her prior medical care was not pursued. In still another DOA instance, the intern asked the wife of a younger man who was brought in dead moments before:

Did he have medical trouble before?

The wife, starting to cry again, answered:

I don't know what it could have been. I don't know what it could have been.

Her remark terminated the discussion of prior medical history.

It is instructive to contrast these forms of lay-medical interaction about illness and medical history with that more commonly encountered format of interaction of the physical examination or taking of a patient's medical history. In the latter setting, the physician is concerned to follow through a given line of inquiry, record reported facts, and seek a consistent and detailed account of the background on the case. So that a remark like "She was in the hospital for three weeks in April" could be expected to be followed, in the usual hospital circumstance, by a next question such as "What was she treated for then?" and that by an additional one until he obtained a sufficient account about the matter in question to premise his own diagnostic and treatment activities. And the account "I don't know what it could be," in an encounter between physician and relative about a recent emergency admission of a live patient, for example, would expectably be pursued with a remark on the order: "Why don't you first tell me what you know and then we can try to see what it is."

Under the auspices of gathering material in a medical history the physician is concerned, as he is not here, with checking information for its consistency, filling out lines of reported data with more detail, assessing the reliability of the reporter's account, ignoring irrelevant descriptions, pursuing lines of lineage in the hereditary medical history, gathering information about the specific character of the patient's former medical treatment, and generally attending that whole range of matters which physicians attend when they are doing medical interviewing, diagnosis, and research.

In his "discussion" of causes or possible antecedents with the relatives of the recently pronounced DOA, or his mention of likely causes with the relative of a recently deceased hospital patient on the medical or surgical wards, his "inquiry" takes a radically nonmedical character. While the sentences he utters may be lexically the same as those he might utter when conducting a medical history interview, they are nonetheless asked differently. They are not followed through; they appear disjunctive; any given question does not appear to follow the previous one so that he need not rely on an "answer" to know how to direct the next remark; they are not recorded; he shows no special interest in any specific question or its answer; he shows no concern to move to another area; he allows any question to be answered rather than interrupt should the answer appear not to address the question; any answer is accepted as just as "relevant" as any other. The line of his "inquiry" is thus markedly set off from "medical inquiry" as a method of eliciting "information." As a first statement, it may be said that in the death circumstance the physician is *making talk.*

Not only are the physician's questions not asked medically, despite the lexically medical reference, they are not heard as medical questions. The same lexical utterance, e.g., "Did he have medical trouble before?" made in the conduct of a medical history interview of a patient's relative, when heard as a medical question will be answered with the concern to address the implied medical relevance of it. Persons routinely attend physicians' remarks about their prior condition or that of their relatives as grounds for offering elaboration, providing possibly useable detail to the doctor, thinking over what they recall in their or their relatives' histories of treatments and symptoms, reporting confusions they have about those histories, e.g., "What one doctor told us but how another said another thing," etc. The very possibility of a medical interview rests upon the mutual sense both parties to it have of the medically relevant aspects of a question. For physicians to ask the kinds of questions they do, like "Why don't you tell me what's wrong with you," respondents must know what it means to answer a medical question, must learn what it is to report symptoms, in sum, must learn how to talk to doctors and hear doctors' remarks. While the domain of interests, concerns, worries, and technical knowledge differs for layman and physician, the possibility of doctor-patient-relative communication rests upon a proper mutual orientation to the sense of each other's remarks.

In examining the interchange between doctor and relative after the death's occurrence was announced and when talk became directed to that fact, I found that the questions that were asked and the remarks offered as answers, regardless of who it was that did the answering or asking, have as their specific character the quality of "making talk" about the event of the death. Utterances lexically similar to those routinely encountered in medical-lay communication are here structured within the framework of a conversational style, so that it can be said of the interchange as a whole that it resembles "mere talk." To provide further illustrations of this character of the interaction, let me give additional examples from the other domains of "topics" regularly found in the announcement of death occasion.

2. *The matter of pain:* The concern over whether or not the deceased experienced any pain before his death is typically voiced by the relative, who asks (and here the specific words employed are extremely similar from one such setting to another): "Did he have much pain before he died, doctor?" In reviewing my field notes on the announcements I have either witnessed or overheard, I find that in only a handful of these occasions did the immediately bereaved fail to form a question regarding the deceased's pain before death. Universally, it seems, the doctor answers, "No," when asked if pain was experienced and in most instances provides a form of "elaboration" which the following recorded comment typified:

> He was under heavy sedation right until the end and I can assure
> you that he experienced no discomfort at all.

With such a comment, the issue of pain is apparently settled. Never did there occur any further interrogation by the relative, nor any greater degree of elaboration by the physician. The striking fact about the "discussion" of pain is its marked uniformity from one particular scene to another. This uniformity is most interesting in light of the fact that the actual circumstances of the deaths the announcements of which I observed differed widely with respect to the extent and manner of pain experienced by the "dying" patient. While doctors therefore routinely lie in their characterizations of the death as painless, more importantly, relatives who in fact knew that the death was painful nonetheless asked the question about pain and let go unchallenged the physician's comment on its painlessness. In DOA circumstances the physician's elaboration on the question of pain usually takes the form of the following comment:

> He probably had a massive heart attack and with these things there
> is hardly any pain because it is so quick.

In one case, a man had a heart attack at home which was witnessed by the family. The ambulance driver reported to me that when he arrived not much pain was experienced, to which he answered, "No," and gave at the home the man was lying on the floor gripping his chest and moaning. The man died in the ambulance on the way to the hospital and was pronounced dead upon arrival. The relatives asked the doctor whether or the account quoted above. The relatives then proceeded to inquire about what they were to "do now" and the topic of conversation turned to the procedures of contacting a mortician, having him call the coroner's office, and the like.

In another case the matter of pain was "discussed" between the pronouncing physician and the wife of a long-term, chronically ill, cancer patient. The woman had spent much of a year prior to the death of her husband at his bedside, long periods of which involved the not uncommon task of having to witness the moaning in pain that often characterizes the lot of these patients. Yet her reference to his pain and the physician's assurance of its absence came off in its typically standardized way, with very little variation from any other announcement of death occasion. She didn't say, as she "might" have, "What do you mean *no pain,* after all I've gone through . . ."; nor did the physician remark, as he "might" have, "You know he felt pain, you certainly saw him suffer with it, cancer is always painful."

3. *Matters of preventability:* In a great number of the announcements I witnessed, the issue of the possible forestallment of the death or its preventability became "topical" via the physician's comment, of which the following is typical, that:

> Of course we did everything we could. There was nothing that
> could have been done at this point.

Such a question was nearly without exception answered by some version of "Yes, of course, doctor, I understand. We appreciate everything you've done." In none of the cases with which I am familiar was the assertion of the inevitability of death "under the circumstances" not provided by the physician nor "accepted" by the relative. At least in my experience, doctors did not qualify their claims that "everything was done," nor did relatives question their not doing so. While it of course happens that legal suits of negligence are sometimes instituted, I am not prepared to consider the manner in which they arise. In the settings with which I am acquainted there occurred no instances where one could detect in the character of the doctor-relative interchange the basis of distrust, suspicion, or anger which might be regarded as preliminary to such a negligence action. Whatever such efforts might have been taken, and my data does not follow through cases sufficiently to locate such efforts, did not seem to be framed within the context of the announcement occasion. To the contrary, the interchange of remarks concerning the death's preventability were uniform with respect to their standardized, almost staged character.

With the above outline of "things discussed" in mind, let me consider, in general terms, the matter of "talking about death," and the "conversational" character of the doctor-relative encounter. If one searches the medical world for that setting where doctors appear to act least like doctors and relatives least like "relatives of patients," the announcement of death occasion seems to offer itself as a paradigmatic locale. The striking character of the doctor-relative "talk" here is that it sounds nonmedical. Concerns for demonstrations to be adequate, for consistency of fact, for completeness, relatedness, relevance—those interests which govern medical interviews, work-ups, diagnostic conferences, etc.—were absent.

The political scientist Oakeshott's analysis of "conversation" so nicely describes the general character of talk in these settings that it deserves a lengthy citation:

> In a conversation, the participants are not engaged in an enquiry or a debate; there is no "truth" to be discovered, no proposition to be proved, no conclusion sought. They are not concerned to inform, to persuade, or to refute one another, and therefore the cogency of their utterances does not depend upon their all speaking in the same idiom; they may differ without disagreeing. . . . In conversation, "facts" appear only to be resolved once more into the possibilities from which they were made; "certainties" are shown to be combustible, not by being brought in contact with other "certainties" or with doubts, but by being kindled by the presence of ideas of another order; approximations are revealed between notions normally remote from one another. Thoughts of different species take wing and play round one another, responding to each other's movements and provoking one another to fresh exertions. Nobody asks where they have come from or on what authority they are present; nobody cares what will become of them when they have played their part. There is no symposiarch or arbiter; not even a doorkeeper to examine credentials. Every entrant is taken at its face-value and everything is permitted which can get itself accepted into the flow of speculation. And voices which speak in conversation do not compose a hierarchy. Conversation is not an enterprise designed to yield an extrinsic profit, a contest where a winner gets a prize, nor is it an activity of exegesis; it is an unrehearsed intellectual adventure.[20]

Oakeshott's analysis, so reminiscent of Simmel's brilliant essay on the structure of sociability, elucidates that key feature of "mere talk," its production in accord, first and foremost, with respect to the conventions of ordinary polite interchange, wherein the "topic" becomes the mere vehicle of expression and not the matter of predominant interest.

In the doctor-relative encounter, the talk which occurs is such that rules of conversation come to govern its production, and the matter being talked about, the death, stands as the merely occasioned topic of conversation. By "occasioned topic" I mean that topic which the occasion provides as the appropriately discussable matter. Physician and relative under the circumstances of a death cannot discuss family intimacies (at least not in DOA circumstances involving a ward physician), the weather, the physician's work problems, the state of the hospital's physical equipment, etc., but their situation prescribes that the death in question be the exclusive "focus of attention." This fact, the required restriction of the topic to death, distinguishes this scene from the pure form of sociability described by Simmel.[21] While Simmel clearly saw the elemental character of conversation as that basic of social activities, his analysis was rather more restricted to the "party," wherein content shifts regularly and requiredly, and the play of "forms" has an essentially artful character. The conversation we find here, in the announcement-of-death occasion, has a severely restricted content; but in constructing talk in a clearly conversational idiom, without respect for concerns for consistency, completeness, medical relevance, and the like, an approach to sociability may be seen. While the content is restricted to be sure, the essential property of the interchange, its conversationally structured sequencing, stands out over and above the fact of the death.

In the announcement-of-death occasion there gradually occurs a transformation from that state of crying, moaning, or distracted silence with which the encounter opens to a sequence of conversational exchange, wherein rules of polite discourse are instated. The prominent feature of the "talk" here is seen in the fact that in engaging in it, acting in accord with the rules which govern polite interchange, e.g., following a give-and-take sequence, leaving the engagement with respect shown for conventional modes of leave taking, distributing the talk among the participants, persons find themselves involved in a recognizable form of regular social conduct. The sheer fact of conducting a conversation in situations where talk might appear a strange activity, namely when a close relative has just been announced as dead, locates the event, despite its tragic character, as a nonetheless handleable matter. In doing "talk," persons affirm their sense of the essential stability of their conditions, for to "talk," where "talk" means abiding by conventions of speech, responsiveness of demeanor, the alignment of eyes and bodies, the exchange of politenesses, waiting for the other to stop before beginning oneself—to do all this is to demonstrate that grasp over one's self that prevails in the ordinary conduct of daily affairs.

The function of "talk" in situations of trauma was perhaps nowhere so elegantly depicted as by Tolstoy in his descriptions of the *Ancien Regime*. In 1805 and during the Italian campaigns of the Bonaparte Revolution, Napoleon is planning his invasion of Russia. In the opening

---

[21] See K. Wolff, ed., *The Sociology of Georg Simmel* (New York: Free Press of Glencoe, Inc., 1950), pp. 40–57.

scene of *War and Peace,* Anna Pavlovna is having one of her famous "soirées," and Tolstoy has her greet a guest, in the opening paragraph of the book, with the following remarks:

> Well prince, Genoa and Lucca are now no more than private estates of the Bonaparte family. No, I warn you, that if you do not tell me we are at war, if you again allow yourself to palliate all the infamies and atrocities of this Antichrist—upon my word I believe he is— I don't know you in future, you are no longer my friend, no longer my faithful slave, as you say. There, how do you do, how do you do, I see I'm scaring you, sit down and talk to me.[22]

Tolstoy's insight, seen in the line "sit down and talk to me," was that in constructing "talk," matters which otherwise might produce severe immobility, upsettedness, consternation, and fear, could be overlaid by ordinary conventions of interaction and thereby have their sense incorporated within and constrained by the requirements of ordinary social discourse. Throughout the first chapter of the book, Tolstoy has Anna Pavlovna engaged in the production of "talk." *War and Peace* can be said to have as one of its central themes the notion that in doing "talk," persons, as members of a society, provide for the stability of the social world.[23]

The institutionalization of "talk," i.e., "sociable" talk or "conversation," here serves to provide a standardized way for bringing the participants into alignment and moving the encounter about from its position of initial disturbance to that point where a consideration of other matters may properly occur, e.g., signing an autopsy permit, arranging for the disposition of the body, obtaining personal belongings, etc. In allowing himself to engage in a conversation, the recipient demonstrates, at least temporarily, his willingness to sustain orderly enforceable forms of interchange, in a relatively bureaucratic setting, with one with whom no other current basis for interaction exists (e.g., the continued mutual crying which two parents might be able to do upon the death of their child

---

[22] L. Tolstoy, *War and Peace* (New York: Modern Library, n.d.), p. 1.

[23] Perhaps his most elegant statement is on p. 704, *op. cit.*:

> As the enemy drew nearer to Moscow the attitude taken by its inhabitants in regard to their position did not become more serious but, on the contrary, more frivolous, as is always the case with people who see a great danger approaching. At the approach of danger there are always two voices that speak with equal force in the heart of man: one very reasonably tells the man to consider the nature of the danger and the means of avoiding it; the other even more reasonably says that it is too painful and harassing to think of the danger, since it is not in a man's power to provide for everything and escape from the general march of events; and that it is therefore better to turn aside from the painful subject till it has come, and to think of what is pleasant. In solitude a man generally yields to the first voice; in society to the second. So it was now with the inhabitants of Moscow. It was long since there had been so much gaiety in Moscow as that year.

when in the privacy of their home, or, at the other end, the technically oriented discussion of medical fact which would otherwise be appropriate, in the case of a live patient, between physician and relative).

An additional way of describing the difference between ordinary doctor-lay medical interaction and the special quasisociable character it takes here, is by observing the use of ceremonial type interchanges. In the hallway of the hospital, I observed doctors greet their patients with "How are you today, Mrs. Smith," to which frequently the return "Fine thanks, doctor" was given, even when the patient was obviously "not fine."

The remark "how are you" can be heard as a ceremonial piece, to which there is a proper ceremonial return, and can be so treated. Or it can be heard "constructively," i.e., *how are you today,* as a question, an answer to which would entail enumeration, perhaps, of one's feelings.[24] In the death announcement, the character of talk has a general ceremonial structuring, the rules governing its production being those useable as the rules of conversation which all members of the society have at their command. Whole sentences are, in standard conversational fashion, produced and returned in units, in a back and forth exchange of "pieces," the content of which seems of less importance than their structure. "What is being said" becomes blurred, and the "how" achieves central relevance. Through their brief interchange of remarks, physician and relative, here standing relative to each other as "anyman," effectively neutralize, for the moment, the radically discrepant character of each's perspective on the event of the death. Each out of respect for the other's position relegates the death to a temporarily subordinate relevance, agreeing to sustain a little piece of sociable talk. At the end of the encounter, the physician says "goodbye," the relative his "thank you doctor," and while once out of the hospital members of the family might well go into a renewed course of openly grievous expression, for the moment, a routinized interaction between strangers has been managed through the use of talk.[25]

Before the encounter terminates, discussion is had about such matters as the autopsy permit (in the case of the deaths of hospital

---

[24] Harvey Sacks pointed out the distinction between ceremonial and constructive hearing and treatment.

[25] Dr. X's *Intern* (New York: Harper & Row, Publishers, 1965), p. 98, gives a particularly humorous example of the use of ceremonials in a somewhat different medical setting, that of the sigmoidoscopy:

> These people come into the office and Dr. Smithers says, "Hello, there, glad to meet you," and without further preamble tips the table down and proceeds to thread a twelve-inch rod up their rectums. Then after they are all over with it, sweating and panting and smarting, too, they stand up and Dr. Smithers says, "Well, splendid, we'll send a report to your doctor today," and the patient almost invariably says, "Thank you, Doctor, glad to have met you," and goes out.

patients) and funeral arrangements. Here we see another form of interaction emerge, it too uniquely suited to the task of sustaining a pattern
of composure, attentiveness to affairs of the present in a bureaucracy,
and, here especially, at least a preliminary sense, on the part of the bereaved, of the continuity of his own life circumstances. That form involves
the giving and receiving of "instructions." The physician is concerned to
obtain an autopsy permit, to see to it that family members understand
their obligations regarding arrangements for a funeral, to arrange for
their securing the deceased's personal belongings, etc. Toward the end
of these encounters, it almost invariably occurred that there was an exchange of requests for information and instructions, e.g., "What do we do
now?" "You have to contact the funeral parlor and they will make the
arrangements for you and take care of everything." "When do we do
that?" "In the morning will be sufficient." "Whom do we call?" "When
you get up in the morning just call the coroner's office and they will tell
you when the body will be released to the mortician." In providing accounts of the need to conduct an autopsy, physicians usually point to the
general value to medical knowledge which postmortem examinations afford, often going into lengthy accounts about advantages to others, how
it is important that a hereditary condition be located, if there was one,
so that other members of the family will be alerted to such possibilities
in themselves, etc.

It is a property of an *instruction* that in giving one, the instructor
provides the instructed with a sense of the continuity of his circumstances. That there will be a morning to get up in, a tomorrow in which
to make a phone call, a future at all, may well be a problematic matter for
the immediately bereaved. In providing instructions on "what to do next,"
the physician may provide or aid in providing a sense that the world will
continue to go on, that there will be ordinarily negotiable matters to
handle, that with death, like other affairs, arrangements must be made,
plans developed, organizations' schedules respected, and the like. Immediately bereaved persons have been observed, in these settings, to
write down notes to themselves on the sequence of steps to be taken as
regards the disposition of the body, to copy down telephone numbers,
and the like.

Physicians have been known to suggest that the request for an
autopsy permit "at such a time," is a cruel activity, that persons suffering
from shock should not be made to attend such matters.[26] It can alter-
natively be proposed that the requirements to engage in such activities
provide the immediately bereaved with a set of tasks, the anticipation and
doing of which help bridge the gap between disoriented grief and anomie
and the continued circumstances of his own life.

[26] See for example, Dr. X., *op. cit.*, p. 78.

SIX

Extensions Outside the Hospital

Notes on a Sociology of Mourning

❦ ❦ ❦ IN THE COURSE of observations which were made at a funeral parlor in Miami, Florida, I observed a woman come into the parlor director's office just prior to the beginning of a funeral ceremony to speak with the rabbi, who was busy arranging last minute details of protocol with the mortician and his staff. She introduced herself by name and as a sister of the deceased (who was a woman in her late forties with several adolescent children). As is customary in Jewish ceremonies, the rabbi was to read off a list of family members who had attended the ceremony, to be ritually presented as those who had assembled to pay their last respects to the deceased. She asked the rabbi to include her name on the list, saying "I was not at the Bar Mitzvah of the eldest" (the older boy of the deceased), this being explicitly proposed as the special reason she wanted to insure that her name be included as among those assembled for the ceremony.

In this chapter, I should like to suggest the sense of such a request by considering how the occasion of a death may be seen to stand as a happening warranting a "family roll call," and thereby as the occasion for drawing the boundaries of social units in general. Certain other events are often treated similarly, notably births, weddings, and divorces. My main concern shall be to try to locate some of the principles regulating the manner in which news of a death is spread to members of the "family" and to others.[1] The material on which the discussion is based was drawn

[1] In nearly every ethnography in which death is treated, attention is given to the way persons spread news of a death through kinship and other collectivities. For

153

from conversation I had with members of deceased persons' families during the period immediately following the death in the hospital, and upon
some observations I managed to make during the time in which others
were being informed of the deceased's death after relatives left the hospital setting.

At least in American society, there is associated with any given person a class of others, partially nameable in kinship terms, who are considered entitled to learn of a person's death in a direct fashion. For
heuristic purposes I shall conceive of a set of concentric rings, surrounding any person A, each circle being distinguished from the others
by the amount of time and the medium in and by which its occupants
can rightfully expect to be informed of A's death. In general, it is possible
to learn a good deal about a person's position in a variety of social structures by mapping out the circles of those persons entitled to learn about
his death.

The innermost circle consists of those persons who are entitled to
learn of A's death in both a direct and rapid fashion. In our society this
set of persons consists of those who are known as members of the "immediate family," a notion I shall explore in detail below. They have rights
to know of the death very soon after it occurs, usually within moments or
hours, and, it appears (at least in the middle classes), expect to be informed either in person or over the telephone. Members of the "immediate family" regard it as improper to inform one another of a death by
letter, or even by telegraph wire. If there is a proper person available
to inform them personally, a son of the deceased for example expects to
be personally informed, as does the wife, parent, and, generally, a sibling.
Telegraph wires are reserved for special occasions, as when no telephone
is available, and despite their urgency, they are considered neither
urgent nor personal enough a means of informing one who is especially
close to the deceased. Informing a member of the immediate family in
person is considered proper, it seems, only if a person can reach him
rapidly, and before he might learn of the death in an improper way. I
shall discuss proper and improper ways of learning shortly.

Under some circumstances, as with the deaths of presidents of na-
tions, any person in the society may feel entitled to learn of the news

---

an excellent detailed analysis of the "day of the death," see J. Goody, *Death,
Property and the Ancestors* (Stanford: Stanford University Press, 1962), pp. 51–55.

It has been a traditional notion in anthropological theory that rituals attendant
upon death reintegrate the social group. Malinowski, Durkheim, Gluckman, Hertz,
Van Gennep, and others have accorded central attention to the solidarity functions
of *rites de passage*. My focus here is rather more limited, namely to the ways in
which a death's occurrence, as a piece of reportable news, can be seen to occasion
various demonstrations of group loyalties. I will not deal with funeral ceremonies
themselves.

rapidly, and intimate members of the family may have only a brief few moments of private access to the news, if that at all. While urgency of informing expectably prevails in such circumstances, a significant difference in medium exists in the informing of "anyman" and members of the immediate family. Prominent persons' deaths may be urgently announced over the radio or television, and while that serves rapidly to inform others, it is not an especially personal way of spreading news. The radio may not be turned on and one may not hear such news before others, but unless one is a member of the immediate family or otherwise especially acquainted or close to the deceased, he cannot say, "How come I wasn't *told?*" Radio or TV is not a way of "telling," or at least is a special way of "telling," perhaps a way of "announcing," in the general sense of that term. Were it the case that with prominent persons' deaths all persons had a similar sort of right to know, radio or TV would not be useable. Rather, mass telegrams or some such method would be employed. There is thus a significant difference in rights depending upon whether the deceased in question is merely "famous" or personally known.[2]

When a prominent person dies, or when a person dies in such circumstances that the announcement of his death might properly be made via the mass media, effort is made to contact members of the immediate family before the public-at-large is informed. Depending upon the particular circumstances of the death and the particular fame of the deceased, such efforts may or may not be successful. In President Kennedy's death, for example, some members of the immediate family did not learn of his death personally.[3] While airline companies refuse to release passenger lists of crashed planes before family members are personally informed. on occasion news trickles out before personal informing is completed.

If for some reason there is concern not to inform a member of the immediate family first, as is the case particularly in prominent persons' deaths, such family members must be isolated, taken away from access to the mass media.[4] When persons die, those not intimately con-

[2] For a definition of "fame," see E. Goffman, *Stigma* (Englewood Cliffs, N.J.: Prentice-Hall, Inc., 1963), p. 68:

. . . by the term "fame" we seem to refer to the possibility that the circle of people who know about a given individual, especially in connection with a rare desirable achievement or possession, can become very wide, and at the same time much wider than the circle of those who know him personally.

[3] "President Kennedy's younger sister, Rose, learned of his assassination today while watching a television broadcast from Dallas, Texas, where he was shot." *The New York Times,* November 22, 1963.

[4] When Kennedy died there was a concern not to inform his children until their mother could tell them herself. They were hurriedly secluded and kept behind

nected with the family may feel as though they are intruders should they
find themselves in a position where they will learn of the death at the
same time members of the immediate family will, or generally, be in the
family's presence very close to the time of the death. In one Cohen case a
person arrived at the hospital when a friend had just died and, seeing that
members of the family were assembled outside their relative's room in
what appeared to be a grieving scene, quietly left without encountering
them. He reported that he didn't feel comfortable being present at such
a moment and would prefer to wait until a more appropriate time to
express his condolences. He felt that this was a time for the family to be
left alone.[5]

It is a general consideration sympathizers have that they must
time properly their encounters with the immediately bereaved. Persons
who lie on the fringe of the deceased's social circle feel some discomfort in offering condolences at a point too close to the death, feeling
that such a time is properly reserved for immediate family members. In
paying house visits on the immediately bereaved, the sympathizer likes
to have some assurance that he will not be intruding upon an intimate
family scene. Generally, information as to the propriety of such a visit is
obtained from one who occupies a closer relationship to the immediately
bereaved. It is apparently quite frequent in such occasions to find certain
persons emerge as organizers of sympathizers. They are usually those who
are close enough to the immediately bereaved to be in a position to speak
in their behalf on matters of protocol, yet not so close to the deceased
himself as to be more properly engaged in active grieving themselves. I
shall have occasion below to consider such a role again.

It is additionally to be noted that while concern is shown for the
death as a "family affair," the occasion may nonetheless constitute a way
in which usually operative rules of social distance are bypassed. It is the
fact that offers of sympathy must be accepted without invitation that
places the more distant sympathizer in a situation of ambiguity, for should
he enter the family scene when only members of the family are present,
he is accepted nonetheless, out of respect for his intent, and can feel that
his intrusion is something the immediately bereaved cannot sanction, a
fact which may make it more strainful. Immediately bereaved find themselves open to receiving persons in a more intimate and less controllable
way than they ordinarily would.[6] It is apparently a custom in large sec-

closed doors all afternoon, away from public contact, until she arrived to tell them
herself. See *The New York Times*, November 22, 1963, p. 4.

[5] In Kennedy's death, *The New York Times* (November 22, 1963, p. 2) reported:
   Newsmen and photographers who were at the Hyannis Airport in Barn-
   stable when the Senator and his sister arrived shortly before 5 P.M.,
   apologized for having to be on hand.

[6] They are, in Goffman's term, "open persons." See *Behavior in Public Places* (New
York: Free Press of Glencoe, Inc., 1963), p. 126.

tors of our society for the immediately bereaved's house to be open in the days immediately following the death. As a counterpart, perhaps, of the wake, and in Jewish circumstances termed the period of "shiva," such occasions lack usually enforced rules governing invitations. The door is left open and all comers are free to walk in and pay their respects. One finds, in such circumstances, an admixture of close relatives, close friends, and mere acquaintances; and such occasions, perhaps by very virtue of the considerable variability in perspective which participants hold with respect to the death, are known frequently to turn out to be sociability affairs.[7]

It can be suggested that the lack of required invitations may also work in an obverse fashion. Persons who might otherwise not be ones who could be invited, may nonetheless arrive at the funeral or the bereaved's home. It is routinely reported in newspapers that famous persons attend funerals of "commoners," especially if the death can have some larger significance than that which it holds for the family. The Vice-President of the United States attending the funeral of a civil rights worker killed in Mississippi is such an example. He could not properly be invited to attend, and in coming therefore bestows some wider significance upon the event.

Returning to the spread of the news, it is to be seen that for some persons there may be no one to tell at all, the only people likely to be aware of the death being those various community health officials whose primary responsibility it is to certify legally persons' deaths and to dispose legally of human remains. On frequent occasions the only persons involved in a County Hospital death were the police, the coroner's office, and staff members on the Emergency Unit. These persons stand in merely an occupationally entitled relationship to the occurrence and news of deaths.[8]

County's physicians attend a conception of a proper order in considering whom to call and whom to speak to when announcing a death over the telephone. They employ a standardized conception of an order, i.e., one which is generally applicable without respect to the particular individuals involved, but for any given death. If it is a child who has died, they request to speak to the father. If the father is not available they speak to the mother and announce the death to her. If neither parent is there, they leave a message and await a call from a parent, except under

[7] Though that sociability may well be a function of the great number of tranquilizers taken and the amount of liquor consumed on such occasions.

[8] It is persons with no locatable families who constitute the major population of such places as county morgues and county-operated cemeteries. There are generally two classes of such persons, those who lie at the bottom of the social class structure, e.g., vagrants, beggars, and the like, who have no locatable family, and those who are the end points of a kinship line, who might nonetheless be prominent, with past families whose members they have outlived.

the circumstance where they know in advance that there is no parent. If it is an adult who has died, and who is known to be married, the request is made to speak to the wife or husband. If that spouse is not there, they choose one of several alternatives: *1.* if the adult who died is old and known to have elderly children, the request is made to speak to a male child, and if no male child is available, to a female child; *2.* if the adult who died has no children nor a spouse, the request is made to speak to a brother, sister, uncle, or aunt, in that preferential order; *3.* if there is no elderly child, spouse, or brother, sister, uncle, or aunt, a more distant relative, e.g., niece, nephew, cousin, etc., will be told of the death; *4.* if there is no available relative, and only under that circumstance, inquiry is made as to whether or not there is a close friend, and that person is informed. Under no circumstance was a person who announced himself as a friend told of the death before a relative was, if it was expected that a relative could be contacted, even if that meant that out-of-town phone calls had to be placed.

When announcing a death in face-to-face interaction, slightly different possibilities present themselves by virtue of the fact that in face-to-face contact, physicians appear to have difficulty in forestalling the release of the information to some pending the arrival of others, for some of the reasons I have indicated above. This is more so true if the person in question insists that he learn what has happened, or appears especially nervous. Should a relative arrive at the hospital, he will be told of the death immediately, without respect for the fact that he might lie, relative to others in the family, in a more distant formal kinship relation to the deceased. Should a friend arrive at the hospital and a relative is expected to come shortly, some effort will be made to avoid telling the friend until a relative arrives. When physicians have some control over the whereabouts of the family and can feel that a person told "out of order" will not relate the news to those entitled to hear from the doctor, they will release information to persons who otherwise would be made to wait.

Some clarification of the notion of an "announcement" is required. It is only with respect to those persons who have a "right to know" that the order of informing is relevant and with respect to whom an "announcement" must be made. Many persons in the hospital "learn" of a death because of their occupational involvement in such occurrences. And in wartime, soldiers on the battlefield "learn" of others' deaths long before members of the dead man's family do. It is only if a right to know exists that one entitled to know might not be immediately told until those having priority rights are informed. These rules have territorial boundaries. If two persons are involved in an accident and one dies, the other will be informed of his death "out of order" if he is on the scene. (It is noteworthy that persons often seek elaborative news of a death from those who are in close proximity to the person who died, and persons who have been in close proximity often feel obliged to render a more personal service to those who will otherwise learn of the death only more formally.[9])

Members of the deceased's family try to spread news of his death in line with their conceptions of a proper order of information release. On the basis of my conversations with bereaved families and the few opportunities I had to observe their behavior after they left the hospital, I can begin to sketch what some of these considerations look like and provide at least a first approximation to how they were handled. Because of the limited number of cases on which the remarks below are based (I followed three families into the home after the death and spent some time with the members of one family who did their telephone calling from the hospital itself), they are to be regarded as only of the most preliminary and speculative character.

The families I witnessed seemed to be concerned that certain persons learn of the deceased's death rapidly, while others need only be told later, and that any given other be informed by one who stood, vis-à-vis the deceased, in a similar formal relationship to the prospective recipient.

In one case a man died, his wife and son arrived at the hospital shortly after the time of the death, and they were informed of it by the family physician. There were two other sons, living in different parts of the country, a daughter living in the same city, and several brothers and sisters dispersed throughout the United States. Additionally, there was a large cohort of more distant relatives, friends, business associates, neighbors, and the like. In making decisions as to whom to call, in what order, and by whom, the following considerations seemed to be operative. The sons and daughters should be informed first, and the son at the hospital proposed that he call one of the sons, have that son call the other, and then he would call the daughter, the expressed concern being with speed: to one son he said, "Will you call Julius while I call Susan." A further instruction, "After you call Julius, will you call Uncle Harry and have Julius call Aunt Sylvia, and I'll call Uncle Sam and Aunt Beatrice," seemed directed to arranging the news spread so that this next set of relatives, the brothers and sisters, be informed all at approximately the same time. It was felt that *1.* sisters and brothers ought not be told before sons and

---

[9] Apparently when persons such as "wartime buddies" announce deaths to members of the deceased's family, they feel obliged to warrant their own interest in delivering the news, and their right to be doing so, by referring to the intimate character of their past relation to the deceased, as is seen in the following fictional example:

> I know you will hear the news from the Army, but I am writing to you because Roger wanted me to tell you if anything happened to him. He wanted his wife to hear about him from a friend and I am a friend. I am also Jewish and I tell you this so you will understand that there was a bond between me and Roger because of that. Roger didn't tell many people he was a Jew.

L. Giovannitti, *The Prisoners of Combine D* (New York: Bantam Books, Inc., 1959), pp. 278–279.

daughters (this was true in all cases I observed except one, where the son in question was a young boy; these rules regarding rights to know and orders of informing seem to hold only if adult recipients are involved), and 2. sisters and brothers ought be told by sons and daughters. An additional consideration, present in several witnessed cases, was that the sex of the recipient was relevant to the manner of news spread. Before placing a call to an aunt, the son's mother (the widow) suggested: "Ask for Paul first and tell him" (Paul being the aunt's husband, the deceased's brother-in-law). When a son at the hospital told the other son to call another sister of the deceased, he instructed, "Why don't you try to reach Sam at work and let him break the news" (Sam being another brother-in-law).

It appears that it was felt improper to have a relative of one kin-class, say children, brothers-sisters, aunts-uncles, cousins, etc., be told of the death of a relative by a member of a kin-class more "distant," formally speaking, from the deceased. This rule seems to hold strongly for the first few sets, i.e., children, brothers-sisters, aunts-uncles, whereafter distinctions between first and second cousins and the like seemed less important. A brother would not inform another brother or sister of their brother's death by having a cousin call him or her, though a son or daughter can properly call a brother or sister, and a brother can call a cousin. There is apparently a strongly operative rule that members of kin-classes not be told of the death by nonkin. While friends were occasionally told "out of the order"—before some of the relatives were—they were neither instructed nor felt properly situated to inform family members of the death.

An interesting fact about the order of informing is that it seemed typical for the relatives closest to the deceased to play very little part in the dissemination of news. In all the cases I observed, and in additional conversations with persons about their own experiences in such situations, I found that wives and husbands of deceased persons did not inform others. Generally, if there are sons or daughters, they informed one another of a parent's death, and widows or widowers did not. In two hospital cases the widow asked to have the physician inform a child of the father's death. In one case in which a young woman died, the husband asked the physician to call her father and tell him of his daughter's death.

In spreading news rapidly to others, informers have the concern not to tell others of the death with a degree of urgency and implied shock value inordinately greater (or less) than is warranted by their presumed emotional attachment to the deceased. An urgent delivery of news of a death says something to the recipient about how it is assumed he stood relative to the deceased, and requires of him that he respond in kind.[10]

---

[10] Just as a casual announcement of death implies some degree of alienation from the one who died, and, on occasion, disrespect for such relationships as obtained

To be awakened in the midst of night with news that someone has died implies that considerable value has been attributed to the relationship between the recipient and the deceased, or the relationship between the immediately bereaved and the recipient.

It is important to note that a consideration in releasing news of a death is that simultaneous with the concern to let those who knew the deceased well be informed rapidly of his death is the concern to inform those closely related to the immediately bereaved, whether or not they are close to the deceased. Bereavement seems to involve as much grieving over the other's loss as over the loss itself, though characteristically different kinds of interests are at stake in the two instances. With respect to most persons, one can find that at some point the import of their death changes in character, for recipients, from a loss those recipients themselves feel to a loss they feel others feel. Deaths have a way of being located as particularly tied to certain persons. So it is said "she lost her mother," "did you hear about Mrs. Jones' husband?" "they lost a child last year." We can notice in examining the way news of a death is disseminated that members of the "immediate family"—brothers, sisters, sons, daughters, spouses, parents—are taken to attend the death as their own loss, and while concern for the welfare of one closest the deceased may be strongly evidenced, each member of the "immediate family" is taken to have suffered a personal loss by virtue of the death. They are all, to some extent, newly bereaved persons. As the news spreads away from kin to friends, business associates, neighbors, and others, it becomes posed as a loss which has occurred for the family, and while such more distant recipients might experience a deep sense of personal loss, they are less likely to feel entitled to regard themselves as in grief. While one can say "a very close friend of mine died," in some sense he lacks that bona fide status as a bereaved that one for whom the tie is based on the person's status as a member of the "immediate family" has.

The "immediate family" can be said to consist of that set of persons who are entitled to a "nonqualified use of 'my'" as a way of describing their relationship to the deceased, where that useage can be employed as a way of warrantably asserting their rights to treatments as having suffered a loss. By a "nonqualified use of 'my'," I intend to refer to the circumstance where one need not add, for example, such descriptive qualifiers as "good," "best," "dear," and the like as required ways of proposing the

between that person and the deceased. Camus provides a classic example of a nonchalant announcement:

> When we had dressed, she stared at my black tie and asked if I was in mourning. I explained that my mother had died. "When?" she asked, and I said, "Yesterday." She made no remark, though I thought she shrank away a little.

The Stranger (New York: Vintage Books, 1958), p. 24.

sense of the death and entitlement to bereaved status. The son may properly say "my father died" and have that assertion warrant others' treatments of him as bereaved, without its being necessary that he employ an
adjectival qualification, e.g., "my good father," "the father whom I loved
so much," etc.[11] While others may and do employ "my," those who are
not members of what appears to be taken as the "immediate family" seem
required, to warrant the death as their loss, to engage in qualificatory descriptive work. The sheer announcement a "relative of mine died" does
not seem to warrant treatment as a bereaved, nor does "my friend died,"
or "my sister's husband's niece died." In our society, at least, there is only
a delimited class of persons who may properly receive treatments as bereaved without providing descriptive accounts of the character of their
relation to the deceased, and for those who must provide such accounts,
entitlement to bereavement is rather weak. Furthermore, it seems the case
that the immediate family is not defined as coextensive with a formally
defined kin network, for only persons who are spouses, siblings, children,
and parents seem to have legitimate use of the nonqualified "my."[12]

Persons for whom the mere announcement of a relational category
does not unqualifiedly provide their status as bereaved on occasion engage in efforts to class themselves as having had essentially similar relations to the deceased as those relations which obtain for proper " 'my'
users." So we characteristically encounter descriptive phrases such as
"she was like a mother to me," and "we were like brothers," etc. These
"category linked" descriptions can be seen as efforts to claim at least
quasibereaved status where a formal position does not lend itself to such
rights. Several possible uses of these ways of talking can be tentatively
suggested. On one hand, their use seems to be a particularly powerful
way of expressing grief, for in contrast to expressions of sympathy which
involve one in an enumeration of the features of the deceased which
"made him such a wonderful person" or of the features of the "close relationship we had," the mere announcemnt of the fact that he stands as a
"brother" suffices to establish or propose the sense of the loss. In situations
of offering sympathy, persons in so describing their regard for the deceased attempt to show their respect for the bereaved via the fact that
they claim a similar relation to the deceased, and thereby have under-

[11] There is a usage, the "beloved mother," which appears almost exclusively in
newspaper notices and ceremonies of death. Rather than being a required qualification, the term "beloved" here seems to be a way in which special respect is
shown the dead.
[12] The hospital nursing manual on regulations on absences for a family death stated:
Three days are granted for death of an immediate family member. Immediate family is interpreted as husband, wife, son, daughter, mother or
father of the employee. One day is allowed for the death of other
relatives.

standing of the event's significance for the immediately bereaved. The usage is a particularly strong conversational device, the citation of the category being a more adequate way of summarizing one's feeling (and also a way of being able to avoid having to mention any specific feelings). It is worth mentioning, as an aside, that the circumstance of a death nicely provides persons with the opportunity for demonstrating their closeness to some social world, via their portrayals of a relationship with the deceased, which could not be as readily demonstrated were the deceased around and potentially able to disaffirm such claims as to the "belonging" of the person in question. The dead can no longer speak for themselves, so claims of past intimacies can be made which would otherwise only be assertable with more attention to the person's possible presence. The opportunity to express grief is an opportunity for the expression of intimacy which the griever might not otherwise ever have.

It was noted that members of the immediate family do not, themselves, spread news of the person's death to those more distant, formally speaking. Insofar as the death is located as their loss, members of the immediate family, in announcing its occurrence to those for whom it does not constitute such a loss, may be seen by others to be soliciting sympathy. There is apparently the concern to sustain the impression that gestures of sympathy are genuinely given, that is, that they emanate from the sympathizer's respect, sense of concern for the family's welfare, and the like, which he without an apparent sense of obligation independently felt upon learning of the death. For the immediately bereaved to impart news of a death is in effect for him to announce his own status as a bereaved, and in so doing he may directly enforce an attitude of sympathy in the other without letting it be naturally exhibited. The recipient is placed in the position of having to produce sympathy on the spot, and that, in turn, may deprive gestures of sympathy of one of their central powers, the sense, at least, that they are genuinely offered. When a death occurs, much may be at stake for the family as regards the degree of sympathy which the community evidences. The family's status, the achievements of the deceased, the circle of his acquaintances and friends, his degree of regard by others, are matters which are taken to be tested significantly by such indices as the number of persons who heard about the death, how many came to the funeral, how many sympathy cards and phone calls were received, etc. These concerns, it appears, can be of paramount significance to members of the family. A "poor turnout" can be, in many instances, as hard a fact to live with as the death itself.[13] While members

---

[13] Any of the features of a "good turnout" can be systematically handled by those who do not want to have the funeral so used. Families who are sure about their own position can insist upon a "private funeral," request that no flowers be sent, and the like. Families who might have reason to be troubled about what a funeral

of the family have strong expectations that others will come forth and exhibit their respect for the family and the deceased, the solicitation of sympathy, by independent action on the part of close family members, can weaken the presumed meaning of sympathy.

Persons who wish to retain their rights to have others treat them as having suffered a loss, and as thereby entitled to treatment as bona-fide bereavers, refrain from taking the task of spreading news of the death, with the exception that immediate members of the family can inform one another of their common loss. The son who calls an uncle to relate his father's death, does not expectably receive "I'm sorry to hear" as a response, but should he call the neighbor, employer, friend, and the like such a response would be enforced directly. There is an additional sense in which he who relates such news, particularly if he does so to those persons in face of whom he cannot, without making them very uncomfortable, show signs of pronounced grief, in some way renounces his own claim to the event's deep significance to him. Those deeply upset by a death are taken to be emotionally incapable of mustering enough composure to set about the task of spreading news to those less intimately involved members of the community. Rather they are taken to be in family seclusion. Not only does a person enforce an attitude of sympathy in another when announcing the death of someone close to himself to someone for whom the death has no such great meaning, but he also, it seems, detracts from the sense that he himself is deeply hurt, a sense better maintained if others can regard him as in seclusion with fellow family grievers.

From my preliminary observations, it seems to be generally true that news spreads in such a fashion that at each level persons of essentially the same formal distance from the deceased inform one another of the death. Friends tell other friends, business associates other business associates, acquaintances tell acquaintances. In spreading news to nonfamily persons, the immediately bereaved generally rely on a snow-balling effect, i.e., in selecting certain key persons to tell they take it that the news will flow outwardly, following a natural ordering based on the relations between persons surrounding the deceased. If there is a set of business associates, after selecting one most familiar with the deceased the immediately bereaved can leave to him the problem of letting those others know who

---

turnout might show as regards the deceased's actual esteem can similarly protect themselves, for in restricting the funeral to a private one they prohibit its being used as a testing ground. And lastly, those whose esteem was questionable can be made to seem greatly respected by purposefully maximizing the turnout. Gangsters' funerals with dozens of cars of flowers are notable examples. For discussion of the "private funeral" in the context of changing American values on ceremonies, and a general analysis of the uses of funerals, see D. Mandelbaum, "Social Uses of Funeral Rites," in R. Fulton, ed., *Death and Identity* (New York: John Wiley & Sons, Inc., 1965), especially pp. 356–359.

should know. They employ the knowledge that the deceased's acquaintances know one another, within certain subsets of persons, and that ones chosen from these subsets will inform others within it. Moreover they select as those to be informed quickly persons who are taken to have the best knowledge of who, within a given domain of others, would want to know of A's death, and they select persons who are likely to know a large circle of A's friends, acquaintances, and the like.

It is an important fact that the occurrence of a death is generally regarded as something that occurs as a unit event, as a happening of the group. That deaths are so conceived is seen in such paradigmatic remarks as "the nation mourns its loss," "the world lost a leader in the death of . . . ," "death struck their doorstep," "the family lost a son in the war," and others. Characteristically, in announcing deaths, offering sympathies, describing the deaths of others, etc., relational categories and the collections of such categories are conversationally employed, e.g., "I'm sorry to hear about your father's death," "his brother died," "closed because of a death in the family." In conceiving deaths as unit affairs, a powerful basis for the enforcement of rights and responsibilities associated with the death of a unit member is thereby provided for, namely, that those rights can become linked to a member's status as a member. Persons who are members of the unit who do not properly respect their responsibilities and exercise their rights can have their status as members jeopardized. This fact can be variously used. Those who consider themselves disaffected from some unit can, by declining to accept their responsibilities and exercise their rights upon the death of a unit member, demonstrate their lack of regard for the unit and their own membership in it.[14] The fact of the linkage among rights, responsibilities, and membership status can also be employed by members of some unit as a way of telling others that those others are not regarded as bona-fide members, e.g., by not granting them those privileges which unit members enjoy. This latter possibility constitutes a key basis for the manner in which news of a death is released.

A first way in which unit boundaries are relevantly tested by a death regards the rules governing release of news. On occasions such as deaths, persons take it that something of a census taking occurs, whereby members of some unit go through a list of the unit's members, and inform each

---

[14] So, for example, when Kennedy died, the Chinese Communists did not send a representative to the funeral, refusing to acknowledge their membership in a world for which his death was taken as an event. See *The New York Times*, November 25, 1963, p. 1.

The way deaths are treated as unit events is clearly seen in the fact that to do damage to a unit, killing one of its members can be an especially powerful device. In the South today it is reported, "white man kills Negro"—such occurrences being attacks on the entire race and not a particular Negro. It is of course well known that the murder of a unit member can be taken as an assault upon the entire unit; not a few wars have been so started.

of them of the death's occurrence. In important respects, deaths are like births, divorces, and weddings, in that each of these "census events" is taken to involve some sort of roll-call procedure, whereby a set of others is notified, invited, or the like. For a person not to be notified of such an occurrence, should he take it that he is a member of a unit for which the occurrence could be taken to have some topical significance, e.g., as a unit affair itself, as a piece of gossip, or whatever, and should he take it that a procedure was undertaken whereby certain of the unit's members systematically engaged in informing others of the occurrence, he has a way of seeing that he has specifically "not been informed." While announcements of death occur regularly in the obituary column of the newspaper, readers of the paper generally do not formulate the notion that they have not been informed of listed persons' deaths. Should a reader have the conception that he is a member of some unit, other members of which, prior to the placing of the obituary, personally informed, in a systematic fashion, a collection of other unit members, then he has available a resource for seeing that he was not notified.

In the case of deaths, a prominent unit is the "family." The "family" is attended as the locus of obligations and rights surrounding the death of one of its members. Persons who regard themselves as "family members," taking it that a systematic procedure for notification was employed in spreading news of a member's death, can thereby have a way of seeing whether or not they were "told." It is by reference to the category "family" that one can locate his own absence, and it is by reference to that category that persons decide who is to be informed in the case of a death.

The category "family" is not to be taken as co-extensive with that entire set of paired relational categories which can be named in kinship terms, but rather has a much more delimited meaning. What it is that elderly grandparents conceive of as the "family" may substantially differ from that conception held by young adult members. It seems generally true that the elderly members of a kinship structure have a much more extended definition of the "family" than do younger members. In one Cohen instance there was an argument between the son of a deceased woman and his father over who should be notified of her death; the son restricted his calls to members of the immediate family, i.e., other children and a sister, and the father urged him to see to it that a whole line of cousins was informed; the son had him see that such persons would learn but that it wasn't their "place to call."

In spreading news of a death it seemed to be a first consideration that those persons be informed who, were they not to be informed, would be able to see that they were specifically bypassed and would have available a way of assigning responsibility to the "family" for having ignored them. What seems to happen is that the spread of news operates within "accountable units," where, for each unit: "immediate members of the family," "distant relations," "business associates," "friends," and the like, delivery of the news of the death can stand as an event which has import for the recipient's membership status in the unit. Throughout the period of time in which the families I observed made their phone calls, remarks on the order of the following were made: "Uncle Sam would be hurt if we didn't call him right away"; "Shouldn't we call Mr. G?" "Mr. H. will tell him, I'm sure"; "Would you tell Harry to tell Ethel to tell the people at the store?"; "How about that cousin in New Jersey, the Schwartz?" "He's Julius' boy, let Julius tell him." It seemed that one could observe, via a stop watch, the process of news spread to each of a successive level of kin and nonkin recipients. The social structure could be "timed."

Merely "finding out" is not sufficient, for in not being specifically informed by the right party, or in finding out only incidentally, persons have, via their notions of the order in which such news is released and their own ranked membership in the relevant unit, a way of seeing that what they took to be their own ranking in the unit is obviously not so regarded. Among a collection of mutual friends, for example, persons rank their own standing relative to each other, such that C might consider himself closer to the deceased friend than that person from whom he received news of the death. Should that occur, and should C take it that A and B knew of the death, and informed E, F, and G, he could see, in learning from those more removed than he regarded himself, that he had been bypassed. When persons related to the deceased might be independent of one another, such an inferential basis would be absent, e.g., if the set of friends was not a "set" but merely some number of unrelated persons. In such a circumstance of nonconnectedness one might properly learn of the death in only an incidental fashion.

The remark of the women in the mortician's study evidences the fact that such unit events can have perhaps a major function in their boundary testing possibilities. Apparently there is a sense in which such occasions can be additive or substitutable, so that having missed one a person can, in attending another, have his membership nonetheless retained.[15] From at least this perspective, a death's occurrence can be said merely to occasion the expression of group loyalties, and, in this sense, is somewhat interchangeable with a variety of other happenings. Among some persons for whom the exchange of gossip is the predominant basis of a relationship, any piece of gossip can serve equally to occasion a demonstration of the intactness of the relationship. That a death might have a similarly occasioned function for some is an interesting possibility.

---

[15] There seems to be a hierarchical organization to such events however, so that missing a funeral can be significantly more disastrous than, say, forgetting a birthday or a wedding.

I pointed out above that members of the "immediate family" tell one another of the death but do not tell others, that constituting a possibility that sympathy will be seen as being solicited and an activity inappropriate for one who must appear deeply upset. There is a set of persons who stand in a special sort of marginal relationship to the deceased and in an "immediate relationship" to the bereaved. Among such persons, the death can be posed as having its central significance in that it is an event which is located as having occurred *for* the immediately bereaved and not themselves, and persons so located, the children of a man whose sister has died, for example, have their entitlement to learn based upon their relationship not necessarily to the deceased but to the immediately bereaved, e.g., their father. It is likely, for example, for a father to announce to his son the death of his wife's sister, and for the mother to announce to the son the death of his father's sibling. In each such case (and this practice was observed in two cases in the hospital), the announcer and recipient do not stand in such a relationship that the recipient would properly offer condolences to the announcer. This seems to be generally true at each point in the dissemination of the news, with the exception that key marginal figures, those who are in "attending" relations to the bereaved, i.e., those for whom the immediately bereaved are, for themselves, centrally located, but are not immediately bereaved themselves, often serve as informational bridges between the immediately bereaved and other recipients. For example, should a husband learn of his sibling's death before his wife does, in relating that news to her sympathy is properly offered him. With the exception of that special sort of encounter, the news is then distributed within classes of persons where exchanges of sympathy, between announcer and recipient, would not properly be expected.

SEVEN

An Overview

❧ ❧ ❧ THIS REPORT WAS, in the first instance, an organizational study, my central concern having been to describe the practically organized work conditions of the hospital environment, and the place of "dying" and "death" within that occupational milieu. It has been a predominant theme of the report that what "death" and "dying" *are* cannot be decided *a priori*, but must be formulated as a problematic topic of research. I hope to have been at least preliminarily successful in providing one set of "operational definitions" of "dying" and "death," definitions which consult the daily judgmental activities of *members of the hospital society* and the social organization of their work. With the topic of "death" as a substantive focus, I have sought indirectly to provide empirical warrant for the general proposition that the categories of social life derive their sense, first and foremost, from the *procedures* which members of the society engage in when dealing with the phenomena of their environment.[1] What has been developed, particularly in Chapter 4, is a "procedural definition of dying," a definition based upon the activities which that phenomenon can be said to *consist in*. While in some respects this was a study of "dying" and "death," it might be better summarized as a study of the activities of *producing* dying and death as meaningful events for hospital staff mem-

---

[1] In another context, that of a public defender legal establishment, I have offered an additional empirical example of this proposition. Official categories of crime, like official medical categories, have their sense provided for in their daily use, often requiring substantial modification in conceptual thinking when that use occurs within the constraints of organizational life. See D. Sudnow, "Normal Crimes: Sociological Features of the Penal Code in a Public Defender Office," *Social Problems*, **12**, No. 3 (Winter, 1965), 255–276.

bers. My attention has been exclusively given to the description of staff behavior in the construction of these categories, a construction which occurs in the course of doing those things which daily ward routines were felt to require.

It was in the course of these routines—handling bodies, administering the demographic flow of incoming and outgoing patients, doing diagnosis, prognosis, medical experimentation, and teaching—that certain patients came to be recognized as persons legitimately accorded special treatments, the "dying" and "death" treatments. In the hospital world, these treatments, organized to fit institutionalized daily ward routines— routines built up to afford mass treatments on an efficiency basis, to obtain "experience," avoid dirty work, and maximize the possibilities that the intern will manage to get some sleep—give "dying" and "death" their concrete senses for hospital personnel. Whatever else a "dying" or "dead" patient might mean in other contexts, in the hospital I investigated the sense of such states of affairs was given by the work requirements associated with the patients so described. For a "dying" patient to be on the ward meant that soon there would be a body to be cleansed, wrapped, pronounced, and discharged, and a family to be told. These activities, and the work requirements they entailed, provided the situational frame of interpretation around such states.

At least one question that has not been directly addressed is that which would ask why hospital personnel feel treatments must be organized on a mass basis. Its answer, I believe, is to be found only in an historical analysis of the development of the medical ideology toward the nonpaying patient, and the peculiarly impersonal environment of the charity institution I examined. I decided at the outset of my investigation to leave unexplained general matters of ideology toward patient care, and to proceed from there to learn something about the ways in which existing practices were organized and what these practices entailed as regarded the occurrence of "dying" and "death." No answer can be provided in this study to such a question as: "Why do they institute social death treatments?" except by invoking organizational requirements. This is clearly a first-level explanation which could readily be pushed back at least one step. Given the predominant concern to phase-out attention to the immediately "dying," and expediently to pronounce persons dead-upon-arrival, I proceeded to examine the character of that treatment in ethnographic detail, documenting the core component features of "dying" and "death" from the staff perspective.

While hospital personnel managed, on the whole, to sustain a detached regard for the event of death, it occurred, on occasion, that routinely employed procedures and attitudes became altered and upset. The successful daily management of "dying" and "dead" bodies seemed to require that patients have a relatively constant character as social types. So long as the patient whose death was anticipated or had occurred was an elderly, poor, and morally proper person, the occasion of his "dying" and "death" was treated with little notice and in accord with ordinarily enforced routines of "death care." On critical occasions, however—when, for example, a child died or a successful, middle-class person was brought into the Emergency Unit as a "DOA"—ordinarily employed procedures of treatment were not instituted, and special measures were felt to be necessary. Nowhere was this disruption clearer than with the deaths of children. Nurses have been known to break down in tears when a child died, and in such cases, particularly, "dying" and "death" temporarily cease to have their firmly grounded, organizationally routinized meanings, activities, and consequences. When an intoxicated or suicidal or "criminal" patient was treated, these persons' moral characters intruded as prevalent considerations in the way in which they were regarded, providing a special frame of interpretation around the way care was organized, over and above that which the category "patient" established. In key instances, patients' external attributes operated to alter the institutional routine in significant ways, causing vehemence, disgust, horror, or empathetic dismay, and, particularly in the case of children's deaths, a radical though short-lived movement entirely out of role on the part of staff members. No matter how routinized an institution's methods for handling its daily tasks, those routines remain vulnerable at certain key points. No matter how nonchalantly staff members managed to wrap patients' bodies for discharge to the morgue, taper off in the administration of drugs and care to the "dying," pronounce deaths and return to other tasks, a special class of circumstances caused these routines to be upset, either made more difficult to carry off, more interestedly attended, or substantially revised.

In regarding these "special cases"—those persons deemed particularly obnoxious and particularly worthy—perhaps insight may be gained into the requirements for usual, orderly ward activities. On those occasions when a nontypical death caused staff members to step outside their regularly maintained attitudes of indifference and efficiency, one could glimpse a capacity for emotional involvement which ordinary work activities did not provide proper occasions for displaying. The maintenance of appropriate levels of affect in the hospital requires an enforced standardization to the types of events and persons which personnel confront. This work of affect management is aided by staff-held theories of proper fate, proper deaths, proper persons, and notions regarding the appropriate role of medicine and surgery in prolonging life and prolonging death. These theories are invoked on a daily basis to support the patterns of care given the dying, the tentatively dead, and the decidedly dead, but they can be employed only so long as the patient in question can be construed to fit the categories for which the theories are relevant. Every effort was made to construct classifications of patients so as to provide for the propriety of treating them in organizationally routine ways, but occasionally there existed a case which resisted that construction. The death of a child, a young adult, and the deaths of those persons who were regarded as morally imperfect, stirred a noticeably atypical degree of moral sentiment. In accounting for the behavior accorded such persons I found I had to fall back upon that vaguely constituted motivational source referred to by sociologists as the "cultural value."

This class of atypical deaths, those occurring for atypical persons and in atypical ways, became set off as the specially noteworthy events of hospital life, the cases which staff members counted for long periods of time and built into stories that were frequently retold when death was made a specific topic of conversation. In selecting certain cases to invest with special meaning, staff members demonstrated that despite their work involvements in matters of life and death, and their routinely casual attitude toward such events, "death" nonetheless held a nonorganizationally prescribed texture of meanings, an event which could call forth grief and empathy. There was a unique attitude which prevailed on such occasions, a qualitatively different style of regarding "poor old Mrs. Smith" who died without incident in the course of the nighttime shift, and that "horrible thing" which happened on the obstetrics ward.

It is to be made clear that the categories "dying" and "death" have very broad currency, being variously used in many settings throughout the society. I have examined only one setting, only one locus of meanings and associated activities. The sense of the categories (i.e., their use) in the hospital, is to be regarded as hospital specific, and while in other domains their usages may share features in common with those found in the hospital, many nonhospital-based uses can be noticed. Death on the battlefield; in the home; in the Bowery; among the very famous; as a topic of conversation; as a legally relevant occurrence; the "death of cities"; these and other domains constitute additional sense-providing contexts of use. While biological death occurs, in American society at least, chiefly within the hospital setting, that setting provides only one of a variety of socially organized worlds within which its meaningful character is provided. What "dying" and "death" procedurally entail among staff physicians within the hospital would seem to share little in common with those activities anticipatorily organized by and consequential for the patient himself and members of his family, those for whom doing autopsies, handling the census of a hospital ward, cleaning up dead bodies, and the rest, are not relevant considerations. My restricted interest in death in the hospital requires that the formulation of the notions "dying" and "death" given here be clearly confined in generality to this highly instrumental domain of technical activity.

There occurred critical junctures at which discrepant attitudes with respect to the "facts" of "dying" and "death," borne of widely differing practical interests, came into contact and had to be managed. The key such juncture at County involved interactions between members of the house staff and patients' families. In Chapter 5, I sketched out the interactional dynamics observed in one such encounter, the announcement-of-death occasion. Here the physician, one for whom the DOA death was just another work event, and an annoying one at that, found it necessary to convey an impression of soberness before a deeply troubled member of the public. While the body was, in the back rooms, being experimented upon and otherwise "processed," in the front office effort had to be made to regard it as a deceased loved one. That the physician at County seemed to experience no special difficulty in moving back and forth between these attitudes of regard and treatment attests, it seems to me, not to what one might be prone to term his insincerity, but to the fact that his situation prescribes the texture of meanings which events of life and death are given. I could find no evidence to support the view that the detachment staff developed in their behavior toward the "dying" and "dead" on the hospital wards in any way "carried over" into their treatment of such matters in other domains. The announcement-of-death encounter discussed above provided evidence, to the contrary, that physicians were well able to move back and forth between the attitudes of "physician" and "anyman." It would be my argument that the conversational posture and strategies assumed by the doctor in announcing the death to the family are available to all persons. Physicians received no special instruction, either in the hospital or in their previous school training, in methods for presenting bad news. That they successfully did so, and did so in rather standardized ways, is explainable, I believe, by reference to the fact that when so doing they acted in the capacity of the layman, and that the requisite skills for gently "breaking news" are skills learned in quite other settings than in the county hospital or the medical school.

My discussion of the interactional problems in settings of bereavement may perhaps be seen as raising some more general issues about the structure of interaction. The routinization of interaction among members of the society requires at some points that basically differing perspectives regarding the sense of an event to be held in check, that each of the parties to an interaction reserve to himself a large measure of the "things he is really thinking and feeling." The rules of politeness and privacy which ordinary civil conversation requiredly obey enforce a special sensitivity by persons to those matters which may properly be shared with others and to which others may properly be subjected, and those which must be contained. Much of interaction can be seen as characterized by essentially the same sorts of interpretive ambiguity found in interaction between bereaved and nonbereaved persons; and what has been seen in the microscopic developmental view of mutual alignment in this setting occurs as a constant, routinized aspect of interaction in a wide variety of social circumstances. A key measure of persons' socialized competence is their ability to spare others their "true feelings" in portrayals of self and others. It is questionable whether even in the most permissive of settings, like the home and the psychiatrist's office, do persons ever manage to fully "let themselves go." It would be an interesting question for research to locate the conditions for a complete relaxation of the concerns for retaining a grasp on one's emotions. The occasion of a death of close and intimately related kin seems only momentarily to provide such a possibility when the immediately bereaved is in the presence of others.

Taking a sequential view of the bereavement process in our society it might be suggested that in contrast to those cultures in which a tightly organized and prolonged ceremonial working through of grief is institutionalized, in our middle-class society at least, the process involves a movement back and forth through a series of more and then less and then more constraining occasions for grievous display. The first key encounter in the hospital, achieving a small measure of "sociated" composure, was often witnessed to be followed by a swift return to tears, as newly bereaved persons left the hospital doors. The ordering, conversational development discussed above, rather than providing anything approaching an "adjustment" to the situation of bereavement, served only as a temporary pause in what appeared to be a protracted bereavement process, a pause required by the circumstances of a semipublic encounter between relative strangers, each with widely differing perspectives on the death.

The method by which news of a death was disseminated, with paramount concern for speed, noncircuity, and little in the way of an attempt to soften its impact, points to the general fact that with respect to some critical facts in the social world, commitment to a "reality orientation" becomes the only properly sustainable course of action. Throughout the course of interactions between physicians and concerned lay persons, the portrayed import of ascertained facts or likely facts is filtered through a series of tactful reconstructions. Accountability to members of the public is circumvented, or restricted within tightly prescribed contractual limits, out of concern for the internal security of the medical world and so as to give interested parties some "room for hope," no matter how hopeless the known circumstances may be. With the occurrence of a death, from the physician's and hospital's standpoint at least, tactfulness, avoidance, circuity, and other devices for avoiding direct confrontation are made inoperable; the facts must be laid bare, no matter what their expected reception or possible organizationally relevant feedbacks. The resources of the institution for doing deceptive work, whether for its own protection or the public's, must, with such occurrences, be suspended. Institutions as well as the individuals to whom they are accountable must be prepared, at some critical points, for telling and hearing the undisguised worst. There are similar "unavoidable facts" in other domains; the businessman's disclosure of bankruptcy, the nation's declaration of war, the jury's pronouncement of sentence. Wherever such a "fact" is likely to occur, one may observe relevant parties to engage, where possible, in some preparatory work designed to pave the way for that point at which forthright disclosure will be required. No matter how successful, however, the physician's efforts to institute "dying" as an anticipatorily attended category, the death itself will always be, in an important sense, "sudden"—at one moment the patient is alive and the next dead. So long as "death" is viewed as having such either–or properties, there will always be a critical point at which a radical alteration of previous states will be perceived, a point at which attempts to construct what has occurred along a temporal continuum will be strained and when matters may no longer be processually seen. It is at that point when, from the physician's standpoint, the "facts are in" and unconcealed presentation is required. (The physician's "sentence of death" is somewhat unlike the jury's in this respect, in that the latter is at least appealable at several levels, and lawyers are known to employ that fact as a way of underplaying any instant bad verdict to their clients.) It appears that only in the religious domain can "death" be construed as a fact of unclear import, with more vaguely defined and hence more variously attendable properties.

Some final comments about the generality of my findings and the peculiar shortcomings of the methodology are called for. County Hospital was the major "charity" institution of a large metropolitan area. In the same complex of cities were some several dozen other hospitals, governmentally and privately supported. While it can be argued that these results hold for a not insignificant institution, findings at County tell us little about the circumstances of care given either in other hospitals for the indigent or, most certainly, in private medical centers. My comparative findings from Cohen serve only to provide some limited restrictions to the applicable scope of the County findings, but precise boundaries of these findings have not been established. Although cases have been reported of "social death" treatments in hospitals throughout the United States, although historical evidence exists that the "dying" have been cast aside and "left to die" in times past, and although the anthropological literature on non-Western societies documents many special treatments given the aged and "dying," the concrete details I have described for County are by no means proposed as being either the same for other hospitals or necessarily a consequence of large-scale hospital organization. County's staff members frequently argued that the reasons for their orientation to "mass care" involved the size of the patient population and the heavy work load of employees in an understaffed institution, but it is in no way obvious that the one follows inevitably from the other. Staff justifications for practices cannot be taken as explanations of them, but stand as the invoked grounds of action.

An ethnographic report of this kind is subject to several possible sources of serious error. My perspective on the world of medical affairs is, in the final analysis, very much that of an outsider. While over a year was spent in considerable daily contact with physicians, nurses, and patients, and while I managed physically to get close to actual settings of medical and nursing practice, what I selected to report upon and, more importantly, the ways in which I came to see hospital events, are clearly a product of my own interests and biases. Being practically involved in the world of medicine and nursing places a perspective around events which no outsider can hope fully to achieve, short of becoming a physician or nurse himself. I can claim only a limited insight into the cognitive life of the medical world, and while some of the considerations which I feel govern work in that world have been stated, there is much which I feel remains inaccessible to the ethnographer.

A more serious and troublesome source of error lies in the implicit judgments of value with which the sheer reporting of "fact" proceeds. The very noticing of a "fact" can be seen as the most problematic of matters. For example, there are numerous references in the text to the "relative lack of privacy" in the treatment of patients' bodies at County. It is quite readily observable, on the public wards, that sheets are not carefully drawn to conceal examinations of patients' "private parts," but formulating that fact as a "lack of concern for privacy" involves a significant judgmental jump. From the perspective of the middle-class observer, the public ward of a lower-class hospital appears public indeed, but the relevance of the "public-private" distinction is not necessarily formulated, nor its features attended, by those persons whose activities I investigated. (It can be suggested, however, that while from the standpoint of the lower-class patient, privacy, in such terms, is perhaps not of great moment, from the perspective of staff, many of whom were of middle-class background, such privacy would be something they would insist upon for themselves.)

While such "choices of fact" represent value judgments of seemingly little import, ethnography is, to my knowledge, continually plagued by the import of such descriptive biases. What often appears as a perfectly obvious "fact" may not, if one insists upon a hard criterion of "fact," e.g., that an environmental feature be a feature which members of the society recognize and orient their actions with respect to, be so obvious a "fact" at all. The chief warrant I can offer for having included the observations I did is that they seem to make up several important themes concerning organizational life and the structure of "death work."